Margaret Gregson

1998.

INTERNATIONAL POULTRY LIBRARY

PEKIN
BANTAMS

Also by Margaret Gregson

With Bantams in Cornwall

PEKIN BANTAMS

Margaret Gregson

Beech Publishing House
Station Yard
ELSTED
Midhurst
West Sussex GU29 0JT

ISBN 1-85736-108-3

Beech Publishing House
Station Yard
ELSTED
Midhurst
West Sussex GU29 0JT

Printed in Malta by Interprint Limited.

CONTENTS

ACKNOWLEDGEMENTS

The author would like to thank the following Pekin
Fanciers for their help, advice, photographs and support during the preparation of this book. These include the following,
with apologies if anyone has been missed:

Ian Allonby.
Tom Corner.
Mr. & Mrs. Hancox
R B Harper
Peter Hinton.
Derick Hoyland.
Teneil Lobb.
Jessica and Lee Manion.
Anne Peutherer
Dick Ricketts.
Eddie Starkey.
Clive Stephens.

My thanks also to the Pekin Club for their permission to
print the *Club Standards.* Special thanks are due to D J
(Derick) Hoyland, the dedicated Secretary of the Pekin Club
who gave much assistance and supplied photographs, including the Champion Hen shown on the front cover and in the
colour section.

CHAPTER ONE.

EARLY DAYS.

Preference in anything is entirely dependent upon the individual's own choice, but in the world of poultry there can be little more pleasing for anyone to look at than a trio or pen of young Pekins. Pekins are amongst the most popular breeds of poultry and their visual impact, painting such a pretty picture, must be more than partly responsible for this popularity. They constantly arouse "oohs" and "aahs" from even the most hardbitten observer when on exhibition at local shows and many are kept by people, not for showing or breeding, but simply because they are so rewarding.

Pekins are the "true characters" of the poultry world, enjoying human contact, inquisitive and always ready to acknowledge and greet visitors with their familiar, waddling walk and eager, expectant little faces. Softly feathered and rounded in shape, with bright red faces and combs, they are surprisingly active on their short, well-feathered legs and feet and give constant pleasure.

But the Pekin shape, or *type* as it is known, that today we take for granted and expect to see in our birds, is very different from the early Pekins first introduced into this

Figure 1.1 Trio of Pekins Outside

Figure 1.2 Mottled; bred in the 1940s

country, and indeed, is far removed from this type of bird bred and exhibited only thirty or forty years ago and well remembered by some of the "elder statesmen" of Pekin breeders, a few of whom are still alive and showing their stock today.

Keeping poultry is time consuming. The days speed quickly by and soon the next breeding, hatching and maybe, showing season is with us once again so that we can scarcely believe that a whole year has passed by and that the circle has begun. Breeding poultry means living in a world of constant anticipation: Will the eggs be fertile? Will the hatching be successful? and, most important of all – will the chicks be of a good type and colour?

We are all so busy and concerned with our own stock, engrossed in our own little world, involved within the cycle, that it is easy to forget that the very existence of the Pekin as we know it today, is the result of the hard work and dedication of the enthusiastic breeders of the past.

Pekins present an image of gentleness and softness and it could be easily thought that they would appeal more readily to women than men, but many male breeders are totally committed to these little birds and the majority of the country's foremost breeders and exhibitors are men. Admittedly, in the early days of Pekin breeding, social factors would have precluded many women from keeping poultry in their own right and early records and accounts of the initial days of the Pekin's evolution, indicate that it was predominantly male breeders who enthused over the breed and who sought, by careful selection, to produce birds of the right type in the required colour, although we know from photographs and drawings that they in no way resembled our Pekins of today.

The first Pekins to be seen in Britain were imported from China in the 1860's following the ransacking of the Summer Palace in Peking during the Anglo-French Expedition. Why the (g) of Peking was omitted in their name is unclear, but perhaps it was originally left off by mistake and the word continued in its new form.

But, as part of the loot from the palace, Buff Pekins were taken and brought to this country. In similar vein to the story of the origin of the kink in the tail of the siamese cat, whereby the princess used it to hold her rings in safe-keeping whilst she bathed, there is a story surrounding the Buffs which is interesting to relate. It was believed that Buff Pekins, being small and attractive to look at, were kept as pets by the Emperor of Peking, and, since yellow was supposedly the colour reserved for members of the Imperial Family, buff being close to yellow in the poultry world, there might be more than a hint of truth in the claim.

The arrival of these miniature birds created a great deal of interest, and during the years following the expedition, some more buffs and then some blacks and cuckoos were imported from China, but in time, most of the original stock died. The early enthusiasts for the breed soon realised that if the breed was to be continued in this country, let alone improved, outcrossing was necessary. During this period, the Nankin and the Booted bantam were used and eventually, by using a black Pekin X white Booted mating, the white Pekin was created.

This was a time of experimentation, often by trial and error, for the early breeders had little or no knowledge of

Figure 1.3 Black Pekin exhibited by Tom Corner

Figure 1.4 W. F. Entwisle's
Pekin Cock in 1889

In no way does it represent the type today.

genetics, but they were dedicated enthusiasts and worked hard to improve both the type and colour of their birds. However, when we look at the drawings of these early birds and compare the results of all their hard work with the Pekin today, we know that the Pekin they produced was a long way away from the standard we accept today.

Seventy years on, in 1933, J. F. Entwisle, the son of William Flamank Entwisle, regarded as the 'Father' of the bantam fancy, wrote about the Pekins that he remembered from his boyhood and recalled that even then, following all the breeding programmes of the earlier years, the buffs had little buff in them and that the black males were very often multi-coloured with feathers of brown and white mixed with the black. The black females too, had problems. Birds were rarely without red in the neck hackles.

Yet the breeding programmes continued. It was decided that a better bird might be produced by breeding down from the large Cochins using Aseel and Modern Game cocks on small Cochin hens. As with any breeding programme it was a lengthy process, but gradually, through good management, careful selection and meticulous, though somewhat primitive record keeping, small, rounded Pekins were finally achieved.

In time the major poultry shows were persuaded to include classes for this new breed and the Cochin or Pekin Bantam Club was formed to promote the breed and to encourage new and young fanciers. In 1933 a handbook was issued, free to all members, in an attempt to give information on methods of breeding the colours as they existed then,

YEAR 1933.

PRESIDENT—Mr. W. H. SILK.

VICE-PRESIDENTS—

Mr. J. H. BROOKSBANK.
" G. L. BOOTH.
" J. W. COUSINS.
" C. M. HESFORD.
" J. JOHNSON.
" F. W. SMALLEY.

Mr. H. SNOWDEN.
" J. SNOWDEN.
" H. HOUGH WATSON.
" H. WHITLEY.
" F. WORSLEY.
" A. YEUDALL.

COMMITTEE—

Mr. G. L. BOOTH, Junr.
" A. P. BREAR.
" C. BROWN.

Capt. L. G. M. WHITLEY.
Mr. G. WHITAKER.
" J. WRIGHT.

CLUB JUDGES (elected March, 1933)—

Mr. W. H. SILK.
" JAMES GREEN.
" J. W. COUSINS.
" G. WHITAKER.
" H. SNOWDEN.
" F. WORSLEY.
" G. L. BOOTH.
Capt. L. G. M. WHITLEY.

Mr. C. BROWN.
" J. S. KIRKLAND.
" J. SNOWDEN.
" J. WRIGHT.
" F. W. SMALLEY.
Major G. T. WILLIAMS.
Mr. J. JOHNSON.

HONORARY SECRETARY AND TREASURER.

Mr. JAMES GREEN, 49, Bolton Road, Silsden, nr. Keighley, Yorks.

ANNUAL SUBSCRIPTION 5/-, payable January 1st in each year

Figure 1.5 Club List for 1933
This shows the main officials for the year.
The quality of reproduction is affected by the state of the original.

and advice on management. The list of club officials for that
year contains names of breeders who must be credited with
building the foundations of the breed today.

We are fortunate today to still have with us, Pekin
breeders who are able to remember those early days, and
who, as youngsters in the fancy, looked up to these 1933
Club members with awe, absorbing all the advice they offered. But, today's Pekin was still a very long way away and
even the birds which won the top poultry awards, were both
too long in the leg and poor in colour by today's standards.

Birds were imported from America, but it was generally accepted that not only were they too large, standing tall
and long in the leg, but that they also conformed too closely
to the American Standard, rather than to the British and
this was not acceptable. Some rather heated correspondence
appeared in the Feathered World of August, 1933, in support
of the British Cochin or Pekin, written by the President of
the club, Mr W. H. Silk.

He argued in favour of the British Cochin or Pekin
Bantam, suggesting that it outstripped the large Cochin for
type and feathering, unlike its American counterpart, and
praised the small contingent of breeders in this country for
the obvious advances made to the breed. He suggested,

> **"Even the past four years has, in my view, seen an improve-
> ment that can only be recognised by those who make a point of
> studying the illustrations of the winners, as I do."**

He recalled from the earlier days a white Pekin cock
that had been unbeaten through three complete seasons. In

Figure 1.6 Advertisement; W H Silk an important
Pioneer Breeder

preparation for his article he had discussed the bird with some "old time" Pekin fancier from Yorkshire, a nucleus for Pekin breeders. They remembered the bird well and, in their judgment, the bird, when the article was written, in 1933, *"would have hardly been in the money in good company today."*

So there is little doubt that both the type and the feather quality in the Pekin were improving rapidly.

In turn, many of our Pekins were exported or sometimes loaned to help the breeding programmes on the other side of the Atlantic. One particular Buff cock, considered to be of excellent type and colour, was loaned to a breeder in the States, sired many chicks there and was returned in time to be shown at the Crystal Palace, where he again won awards for his owner. There were few restrictions and regulations then over movement of livestock and consequently, it was common practice to export birds, not only for breeding, but also for showing. Major G.T. Williams reported in the 1933 handbook as having been elected a Club judge and who lived at Tredrea Manor, between Truro and Falmouth in Cornwall, ran a successful business exporting ornamental poultry. Adverts for his stock appeared regularly in *The Feathered World*, as did stories of the excellent quality of the Pekins that he supplied to fanciers as far away as Egypt.

During the 1930's, the poultry fancy was very popular and shows held in this country were numerous. It was considered unnecessary for the competitors themselves to travel the long distance to the shows. Their birds were carefully boxed and sent by rail to venues all over the country, where they were met at local stations by show stewards. Once shown and judged, the birds were re-boxed and returned

Cock

Hen

Birchen (also known as Greys (OEG) and Silvers (Sussex) in other breeds. (Courtesy: Derick Hoyland)

Non–Standard Colours

Buff Hen (Club Champion)

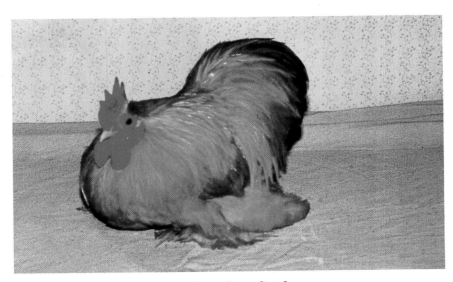

Buff Pekin Cock
Both Courtesy Peter Hinton

Columbian Group

Head of Columbian Female showing striped hackle with white margin

Columbian Pekins

Cuckoo Pekin Cock

Barred Hen
Both Courtesy Derick Hoyland

Mottled Pekin Cock
Courtesy: Ian Allonby

Mottled Pekin Hen
Courtesy: Eddie Starkey

Cock
Courtesy: Ian Allonby

Hen (Courtesy: Eddie Starkey)
Partridge Pekins

Black Pekin Hen
Best True Bantam at the Stafford Show
Courtesy: Anne Peutherer

Black Hen Bred by the Author

Cock

Hen

Silver Pencilled Pekins (Courtesy: Eddie Starkey)
Non–Standard Colours

White Pekin Hen
Derick Hoyland's Reserve Champion at Stoneleigh
Also on outside Cover

White Pekin Cock
Courtesy: Eddie Starkey

Blue Pekin Cockerel

Blue Pekin Hen
Both Courtesy Derick Hoyland

Hen
Best Pekin at National Show. Courtesy: Peter Hinton

Prize Winning Hen
Bred by Author

Lavender Pekins

Red Pekin Hen
Courtesy: R B Harper

Markings of Crele Cock
Orange/Yellow (Derick Hoyland)

Non-Standard Colours

Trio of Lavender Pekins (The Author)

Breeding Pen of Non-Standard Birchen Colour
(Derick Hoyland)

Splendid Black Cock
(Courtesy: Derick Hoyland)

Lee & Jessica Manion & Their Buff Pekin

Barred Pekin (Cochin) Cock

Black Cock

USA–Type Cochins
Differ from British types; called Cochins in USA like the Large.
Courtesy: J E Harris

London Zoo: Children's Area

Note the Pekins & Red Jungle Fowl Cock

Chas. M. Hasford

Oakdene, Ormskirk,
Lancashire

Telegrahic Address. Hesford Ltd,
Ormskirk, 'Phone No. 64.

BLACK PEKINS

Miss E. Holt

Trevalyn Manor, Rossett,
Denbighshire

BUFF PEKINS

Telex 31, Rossett
Station Rossett G.W.R.

Figure 1.7 Advertisements from the 1933 Period

Pekin Bantams

Class 44. Cochin or Pekin, Black. Male.

920	E. Turner	
921	James S. Lord	
922	Stephen B. Airey *SECOND*	
923	W. Horner *FIRST*	£50
924	J. Wright	
925	T. L. Corner	
926	T. E. Croft *THIRD*	
927	P. Lockwood	
928	G. M. Hesford	

929	W. H. Silk	£15 15s.
930	G. M. Hesford	
931	F. Swindells	N.F.S.
932	John Mellor	N.F.S.
933	F. Swindells	N.F.S.
934	Mrs. R. H. Gregory	N.F.S.
935	A. P. Brear	
936	R. J. Clifford	

Class 45. Cochin or Pekin, Black. Female.

937	James S. Lord	
938	Stephen B. Airey	
939	W. Horner	£50
940	Stephen B. Airey	
941	W. Horner	£50
942	C. P. Foster	N.F.S.
943	J. Wright *FIRST*	
944	John H. Gee	N.F.S.
945	J. Wright	
946	T. L. Corner	
947	T. E. Croft	
948	G. M. Hesford	
949	W. H. Silk	£15 15s.
950	G. M. Hesford	

951	F. Swindells	N.F.S.
952	John Mellor	N.F.S.
953	D. P. Davies	£20
954	L. Hirst	
955	D. Holmes	
956	G. L. Booth	
957	Mrs. R. H. Gregory	N.F.S.
958	A. P. Brear	
959	Mrs. R. H. Gregory *3RD*	N.F.S.
960	R. J. Clifford *SECOND*	
961	R. H. Wilson	£5
962	R. J. Clifford	
963	R. H. Wilson	£5

Class 46. Cochin or Pekin, White. Male.

964	Stephen B. Airey	
965	W. Horner	£50
966	Fred Bancroft	£10 10s.
967	Master H. J. Vine	
968	J. W. Cousins	
969	John H. Gee	N.F.S.
970	T. E. Croft	
971	John H. Gee *3RD*	N.F.S.

972	T. E. Croft	
973	W. H. Silk	£15 15s.
974	E. Porter *1ST*	£20
975	G. L. Booth	
976	M. Jackson	
977	G. L. Booth	
978	J. Lyon *2ND*	

Clasa 47. Cochin or Pekin, White. Female.

979	H. Binns	
980	Stephen B. Airey	
981	H. Binns	
982	Stephen B. Airey	
983	W. Horner	£50
984	C. P. Foster	N.F.S.
985	Fred Bancroft	£10 10s.
986	Master H. J. Vine	
987	Fred Bancroft	£10 10s.
988	J. W. Cousins	

989	J. Wright *1ST*	
990	W. H. Silk	£15 15s.
991	J. Wright *2ND*	
992	E. Porter *3RD*	£20
993	W. H. Silk	
994	E. Porter	
995	W. H. Silk	
996	G. L. Booth	
997	M. Jackson	

Figure 1.8 Examples of Classes, Results, Prices

safely to their owners. Surprisingly few birds went missing, for great care was taken of the exhibits. Sam Lean of Cornwall, recalls that at some of the larger shows in the West Country, being a youngster, he was often given the job of looking after the precious exhibits and many times he ate and slept with the birds in his care.

Occasionally snippets of information can be found in some of the early poultry magazines, with a letting off of steam by some irate fancier. There is one story of an exhibitor who, having sent off his bird to the British Bantam Association Show in 1949, safely collected his returned Pekin from his local railway station. Living some three miles away, he tied the box onto the parcel rack on the back of his bike and set off on an uphill journey home, only to discover that the bird in the box did not belong to him. His had been sent elsewhere, and, poor chap, it appears that he never did manage to trace the whereabouts of his bird.

When we look back into the social history of the 1930's, and realise that it was a time of deep depression, unemployment and that money was tight, it is somewhat amazing to see how well the shows, held all over the country and abroad, were supported. Even if the birds were sent alone by rail, it would be costly, yet old show catalogues indicate that the exhibitors were from far and wide. They were also prepared to advertise the sale of their stock in both show catalogues and poultry magazines, which must have been expensive. It clearly was a suitably lucrative hobby, for the cost of good quality stock was high.

But success on the showbench was not of paramount importance. The main and by far the most important aim

amongst the fancy, was to perfect the Pekin, to breed a bird
of good type, with breadth in breast and cushion, good feather
quality and sound colour. Breeders were prepared to pass
birds between themselves, to loan stock and share information and theories on the progress that was being made, and
many firm and long-lasting friendships were made. Yet,
once at the showbench, friendships were forgotten. Rivalry
was strong and competition fierce as each sought to win the
coveted "best of breed" and "best of colour" trophies. Correspondence between them was important, for few then had the
benefit of the new invention of the telephone, or, as the old
advertisement states, "a telephonic address."

However, with the onset of war in 1939, breeding programmes came to a halt and much of the early progress in
the development of the Pekin regressed, and by 1945, when
servicemen returned home, good birds were in short supply.
Small pockets of breeders, however, had managed to keep
going. The Yorkshire contingent was notably enthusiastic
and despite the difficulties and restrictions of wartime, did
attempt to hold as many shows as possible. One such show,
the two day Bradford Bantam Show, was held and a consid-
erable amount of money raised for the Spitfires. As many
competitors as were able, attended, one being John Gee who
made the long, uncomfortable journey from Cornwall, by
train, suffering all the wartime regulations of blackout and
the discomfort of no heating and a journey that must have
seemed endless. Dedication indeed!

As a general rule the Pekin fanciers from Yorkshire are
remembered as being quiet and helpful, but all had a hate of
the fancier they called "Teamsters", the exhibitors who pur-

chased expensive birds to win at shows and who rarely bred any stock themselves. The Yorkshire "Boys" did everything they could to make sure that the "Teamsters" were unable to acquire stock, sometimes unfortunately, at the expense of the genuine novice breeder.

A lovely story comes from Brian Carlos about the appearance of a new face at one of the shows within the Yorkshire circuit. This exhibitor marked his pens by placing some blue granite chippings amongst the litter.

One of the Yorkshire wits peered into the pen. "Your grit's a bit on't big side i'nt 't lad ?"

Within minutes every pen on that side had blue granite chippings amongst the litter, picked up from the side of the road.

Methods amongst the early fanciers were kept to themselves and today would be frowned upon. One kept his Pekins in a brooder until fully grown, with only a little headroom, the theory being that they would never stand high in a show pen. Keeping one strain for selling and another for themselves was common practice and consequently many had breeding areas where visitors were not welcome.

The now demobbed fanciers acquired stock, re-started their abandoned breeding programmes and revived the shows. We can learn a great deal about the fancy by studying the show catalogues from those post-war years. The practice of including the prices of birds that were for sale continued and they also provide evidence of the renewed support for the breed in well entered classes.

Now that good stock was precious and hard to come by, prices were high and some valuable breeding birds not for sale. At the British Bantam Association Show held at Ilkley, in 1949, some of the now familiar, well-known names of the past, were once again in competition: Airey, Silk, Hesford, Clifford, the promoted, now Colonel G.T. Williams and, still in competition today, Tom Corner. It is interesting to notice the asking price of the winning bird in Class 44, No 923, owned by W. Horner. £50 -- Remember that this was 1949! The bird shown on the front of the catalogue is a mottled hen of excellent type, owned and bred by Dick Clifford. She won numerous prizes and for markings, would be amongst the winners today.

This bird, though, was an exception. Even at the largest show held, the three day Dairy Show at Olympia, where the prize money was at one time, as high as 500gns, the winning Pekins still fell short of today's accepted type and had a long way to go. Tom Corner, who was showing at the time, recalls:-

"Then, not only did the birds lack type, they also failed in the quality of the feathering which was brittle, did not bend and snapped easily".

More restrictive travel procedures, the increased cost of feed, (which undoubtedly led to the demise of the large fowl) and the outbreak of Fowl Pest in the 1950's, led to fewer large shows, though the smaller, local events continued to flourish.

In the 1970's a decision was made, following much discussion, that the Pekin Club was ready to stand alone. The aim of the club was, not to breed or exhibit birds of "Cochin" type, and the word was dropped from the official wording. The Pekin Club had continued to grow and, with it, the popularity of the breed.

Today, enthusiasts for the Pekin include not only those solely concerned with breeding and showing, but also, many, many more who keep the breed simply because they enjoy them.

Figure 1.9 Mottled Hen: winner of numerous prizes

**Figure 1.10 Examples of Birds from the Very Famous
Stock of Col. Williams (1930s)** *See Chapter 2.*

CHAPTER TWO

WHO KEEPS PEKINS?

FACES - PAST AND PRESENT

If Pekins are such a popular breed, just to whom do they appeal and who keeps them?

In the past, many a lad out on his delivery round, either on foot, or on his bike, acquired his first chickens by coming across some about to be killed off. Sometimes rescued by the exchange of precious pocket money or given as a gift, these birds would be gleefully accepted and transported back home, journeying in the delivery basket on the front of the bike, or strapped to the carrier on the back. Sometimes, they travelled the distance precariously, not in the safety of a box, but buttoned inside a jacket. Rescues such as these often lay the cornerstones of a lifetime in poultry.

My own grandfather acquired his first bantams in a similar way at the age of ten, in 1900. Although he was brought up on a farm, his family also ran a butchery business from the sixty acres at Zelah, near Truro. Even at the tender age of ten, Tom was skilful with horses, and was expected to work with them and to drive the pony and trap to the surrounding cottages to deliver meat to his father's customers.

One day, he discovered a customer's son aiming small stones at two frightened bantams which were tied by the leg to a kitchen chair. Always a man of quick temper, Tom at ten, didn't consider the size of the tormentor. He reigned in the pony, leapt upon the youth, delivered two black eyes and a bloody nose, grabbed the birds, buttoned them inside his jacket for safe keeping and continued his round.

When he finally arrived home, he had a reception committee of an irate father of the boy, together with his own furious father who had lost a good customer because of Tom's rescue mission. The birds were a deep, reddish brown in colour and, knowing little about chicken, except that the large ones that roamed the farmyard, provided eggs, Tom made enquiries and discovered that they were Rhode Island Reds. He made a coop and a run for the rescued pair and in time, was given a cock bird by another customer. He kept Rhode Island Reds until he died at the age of 94, his final rooster outliving him by six years to reach the grand old age of sixteen. Is this a record?

Similar stories exist of how people acquired their first Pekins at a young age with very precious pocket money and it appears that Pekins, then, as now, appealed to people from all walks of life. Mr T.C. Riley, writing in recent years in a Pekin Club newsletter, recalled that in the 1930's members of the then Cochin or Pekin club included a vet, a doctor, businessmen and one gentleman with the magnificent name of Royal King, who was a town ratcatcher.

Social conduct before the Second World War still determined that a woman's role was to be a homemaker and that her energies should be directed towards the needs of her family. There are few references to women being involved with Pekins at that time, though interestingly, a Miss E.

Holt, of Trevalyn Manor, Denbighshire, must have been an "avant-garde" fancier, for she advertised* her buff Pekins in the 1933 Handbook of the club. In later years, Mrs Airey worked alongside her husband Stephen, becoming both Secretary and Treasurer in the late 60's to the club, on the death of her husband.

Pekins were popular throughout the world. Colonel Williams of Tredrea Manor in Cornwall was, perhaps, this country's foremost exporter of ornamental and exotic poultry. An article in a 1934 edition of the *Feathered World*, was submitted by a Mr H. Holbawy, giving the readers information about his black Pekins which he kept under the shadow of the pyramids in Egypt. He proudly included a photograph of his beloved birds, which unfortunately has aged and faded too much for inclusion in this book, but the birds, far too long in the leg, were supposedly, then, of excellent type. These black Pekins had been supplied by Colonel Williams who had the reputation of exporting only the very best.

Mr Holbawy wrote:

"Everyone who has bantams seems to have imported them from Colonel Williams"

Mr Holbawy had two pens of black Pekins and wrote of them:

"Some of the finest birds in the country, with offspring as fine as the original birds supplied."

It seems that at that time, (1933-34), Pekins were the favourite breed in Egypt, taking precedence over the Japanese Bantam. Black was the most popular colour because, although buffs were greatly admired, they did fade badly in the sun. The breeders in Egypt, however, were not without

*See page 17 for copy.

their problems. Birds suffered from the tremendous heat, were worried by mosquitoes and were the favourite prey of wildcats which roamed the area.

Keeping Pekins has, for many, been a hobby which has been handed from generation to generation. Youngsters acquired knowledge and skills by watching and listening to their elders without fully realising that they were being involved in the learning process themselves.

As noted earlier, Mr J.F. Entwisle remembered the processes that his father (Wm Flamank Entwisle)* had to go through in his attempts to breed down the Pekin from the Cochin by using Game birds as an outcross, finally providing us with the antecedents of our black, white, buff and partridge Pekins. His father was a pioneer in the breeding of Pekins, a dedicated enthusiast, so it was little wonder that the son continued the father's work.

A more recent and still remembered breeder of Pekins was Dick Clifford, from Cornwall. Dick came from a family already heavily involved with poultry, his uncle being the renowned John Clifford, breeder and exhibitor of the Malay. Shortly after the 1914-18 war, John gave his young nephew Dick, some black Pekins. Unfortunately, one hen died, but the gift had given the young boy his start and had kindled his enthusiasm for breeding birds of his own. He had watched his uncle handle and prepare for showing his Malays, and now he was eager to put his knowledge to work for himself, albeit with a different breed. He accompanied his uncle to the Bodmin Show, where, for the first time, he had entered his Pekins. We do not know if he was in the prize

---

* See *Bantams* where the experiments in breeding are described in some detail.

Figure 2.1 Illustrations of Early Pekins by Ludlow a
Victorian artist
From *Bantams* (Beech Publishing House)

money, but it is doubtful, for the birds were not wonderful examples of the breed, but his obvious interest, overwhelming enthusiasm and the numerous questions he constantly asked, attracted the attention of another exhibitor at the show. Admiring the boy's quest for information, he sent young Dick some black Pekins from his own stock.

That man was Charles Hesford, another most successful breeder, judge and exhibitor of his time. Dick Clifford's subsequent lifetime success as a breeder, exhibitor and judge of Pekins began with that initial gift from Chas. Hesford and from that day, he never looked back. During the years that followed, Dick Clifford and Chas. Hesford worked closely together - Dick producing excellent black female Pekins, whilst Chas was renowned for his males.

Dick also successfully bred and showed mottled Pekins taking most of the major awards, not only for the breed, but also the coveted *best in show* on numerous occasions.

Following Charles Hesford's death, Dick Clifford lost the male side of the breeding line and, as he himself aged, he began to concentrate more on judging. He became well known internationally as both a breeder and a judge, travelled to America and corresponded with fanciers from all over the world.

Dick Ricketts remembers Dick Clifford as being very much a "hail fellow well met" type who loved a good chat. One year, when he was judging at the Ally Pally Show, a number of Pekin fanciers followed him round. He couldn't resist having a chat with them as he carried out his duties and he was soon at odds with some of the members of the Club. This was Dick's natural exuberance and love of his

Figure 2.2 Black Pekin: owned by Dick Clifford

hobby showing through, as those who knew him well realised, but the Club did lose a couple of members.

In turn, Dick handed down his enthusiasm and knowledge to the next generation in his family. His nephew, Clive
Stephens, inherited the breeding lines of his uncle's Pekins
and he himself is well known as a judge and successful
breeder of black, white and mottled Pekins.

Another young enthusiast, rather like the young Dick
Clifford years before, is Nick Smith. As a boy, Nick was
eager to learn everything possible about Pekins and he had
in Dick, perhaps the best tutor of the time. He asked endless
questions and absorbed all that Dick could teach him, until
finally, Dick announced that there were to be no more questions. Nick now knew, to quote Dick, "More than I have
forgotten." Today, Nick Smith is a recognised authority on
the Pekin, judging at the major shows and is respected for
always thoroughly handling the birds that he is assessing
and for his wide knowledge on genetics and colour breeding.

One name which appeared frequently in the early show
catalogues is that of Tom Corner and we are fortunate that
today, he is still able to breed and exhibit his Pekins. Able
to remember the early years of Pekin breeding, he is the
source of a wealth of knowledge on the craft of the fancy: on
managing and showing Pekins with success. Eddie Starkey
remembers seeing Tom handle a mediocre Pekin belonging to
a young exhibitor, who had asked "his hero" for his opinion of
the bird. According to Eddie, Tom pushed a feather here and
pulled another there and suddenly, the bird looked a winner.
The young lad was delighted and, no doubt, will remember
the precious advice given all his life.

Tom is now in his eighties and has just been awarded the Certificate of Honorary Life Membership of the Poultry Club for services rendered to the fancy. He grew up in the company of breeders whose names are now legend on the lips of today's fanciers: Silk; Hesford; Cousins; Green.

In fact, Tom acquired his first Pekins from W. H. Silk of Haslemere in Surrey. He attended as many shows as possible, asking endless questions in his attempts to learn about the breed, but, with the outbreak of war in 1939, in keeping with his contemporaries, he had to put his precious birds aside. He joined the R.A.F. and on demobilisation in 1945, still full of enthusiasm for Pekins he couldn't wait to attend the shows to see for himself, if anything had changed.

He was noticed at one show by Chas. Hesford, who remembered the earlier, endless questions of this keen, young man. Learning that Tom was eager to begin breeding again now the war was finally over, he gave him a pair of black Pekins. It does seem that as well as being an enthusiastic exhibitor, Charles Hesford was genuinely more interested in promoting the fancy, especially in improving the black Pekin, than in winning. He had already helped Dick Clifford and no doubt, there are many others who can attribute their beginnings in the fancy to this man.

Tom Corner continued to breed and show only black Pekins, specialising only in this colour until he retired in the mid seventies. Finding then that he had more time to spend on his birds, he added whites to his stock.

Tom considers that today's birds are one hundred per cent superior to those that were bred and shown when he first began in the fancy. Then, the Pekin was lacking both in type and quality of feather, the latter being too brittle. However, he is far from complacent about the Pekin today and considers that there is still a very long way to go before we can be satisfied with the progress we have made. He, like many, knows that there must be more work carried out with the colours, where, he believes, too many breeders have willingly sacrificed type.

Dick Ricketts, known for his earlier articles in the popular *Fur and Feather* and who now contributes to *Fancy Fowl,* joined the Pekin Club in the early fifties, when the five bob subscription took him nearly two hours to earn. He kept Pekins for years and enjoyed them, but decided to concentrate on his first love, Buff Rocks, so gave them up. He reckons that the deciding factor in this was when he returned home one day, to discover that a newly hatched chick had been strangled by its mother's thigh fluff. He remembers how very upset he had been. However, a few years later, he was given a trio of Buff Pekins as an unexpected Christmas present. The birds had been saved from an untimely end when their previous owner died. Dick rejoined the Club and became its Secretary for a few years. Incidentally, the birds were very fine, and Dick later won the Buff Cup at the Reading Show with a cockerel bred from them. Today, Dick Ricketts is a well known judge within the fancy.

One of the characters in the Pekin world amongst today's breeders and exhibitors, is Ian Allonby, from Cumbria. Well known at the major shows, and easily identifiable by his deer stalker and bow tie, he has been a Pekin enthusiast since a boy, specialising in the partridge, lavender and buff. He admits that, whilst his friends at school had posters of

Figure 2.3 Black Pekin of the 1920s
From an old photograph

Figure 2.4 Trio of Black Pekins in the 1930s.

the latest pop idol pasted up in their bedrooms, his walls were covered in photographs of the top breeders and winning Pekins. He has carefully filed away Pekin related publications and old newsletters which reveal much about the Pekin fancy of the past and which have been invaluable in the preparation of this book.

The present Secretary of the Pekin Club is Derick Hoyland, from Barnsley. Involved all his life with poultry, it wasn't until 1976 that he purchased a pair of blue Pekins for his young daughter. Like so many, he fell for these gentle, soft birds, purchased a pair of cuckoos and three blacks for himself and set out to learn more about the breed. Today, he keeps most colours and is a regular winner at the major shows.

However, the faces mentioned so far, have all been involved with the world of showing and breeding and we know that, many Pekins are kept by fanciers who just enjoy them. Today, as in the past, Pekin lovers are drawn from all walks of life:- bank managers, carpenters, solicitors, auctioneers, miners, shop assistants, retired couples – the list is endless.

Pekins are eminently suitable for children. Their smallness and comparative docility means that children are well able to handle them without the problems usually associated with keeping the more flighty birds.

One such owner is Teneil Lobb, who lives here in Cornwall. Familiar with poultry, for her father keeps Frizzles and Minorcas, and sufficiently interested in them to help with the feeding and cleaning out, she had not thought of keeping a breed of her own. Her introduction to Pekins, like my own, began with an egg.

Her mother's employer, a retired colonel, had lost his bantams to a fox. Acting as a go-between, Teneil's mother brought to work some Pekins for him and they spent the day in a box beside her desk. During the afternoon the hen laid an egg, which, when placed in the home incubator, duly hatched. Thus Fred, the lavender Pekin cockerel, was born and he spent many an evening being stroked, whilst seated on Teneil's lap in front of the T.V. In time, Fred needed a mate, and Freda was acquired, providing Teneil with many chicks which in turn have found homes as pets.

Lee and Jessica Manion, from Malvern, were introduced to Pekins when some buffs were added to the family's pet stock of rabbits, ducks and Buff Orpingtons. Being small and easier to handle than the larger Orpingtons, the Pekins soon became firm favourites with the children.

Again, because of their small size, Pekins are very suitable as a breed, not only for children, but also they may be kept by anyone who is confined to a wheel chair. More flighty and active breeds are difficult for someone with limited mobility to control. There is always the bird determined to escape either by flight overhead or the speedy dart to the side, and quick reactions are needed to waylay the recalcitrant rascal. How much more difficult it is to be in control when you are confined to a wheelchair.

Choice of the right breed is so important if disabled young people are given the opportunity to keep poultry and, more importantly, to continue with the hobby for many years. Early enthusiasm can so quickly be dampened simply because the child is unable to cope.

As Pekins can be housed inside, pens suspended from

cause the child is unable to cope.

As Pekins can be housed inside, pens suspended from the walls will give adequate room for chair and legs to fit right underneath so that direct access to the pen is no problem.   Careful thought and planning will ensure that the pleasures to be gained from keeping Pekins are available to all.

Figure 2.5 Drawings of W H Silk's Birds in the 1930s
At this stage the modern type were beginning to emerge, showing the low, forward carriage with the correct tilt.

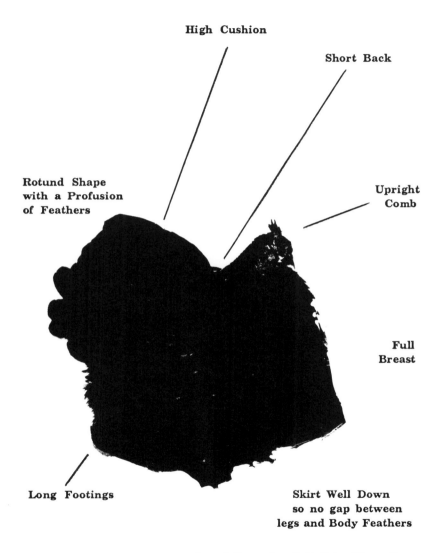

High Cushion

Short Back

Rotund Shape
with a Profusion
of Feathers

Upright
Comb

Full
Breast

Long Footings

Skirt Well Down
so no gap between
legs and Body Feathers

Figure 2.6 Essentials of Standard Pekin Female

Figure 2.7 Essentials of a Standard Pekin Male
Similar to female (Fig. 2.6), but heavier built, taller comb, firmer
tail feathers, and bulkier shoulders

CHAPTER THREE

THE "TYPE"

Throughout this book and indeed, whenever there is any discussion about the Pekin, the word TYPE is constantly used. We have read in a previous chapter, that in the early days of the fancy, Pekins were considered poor in TYPE, when compared with today.

So, when this word is used in reference to the Pekin, just what does it mean and how important is the term? The fact that it is used so frequently seems to indicate its importance.

It is an all embracing term used by the Pekin fancy to describe the overall shape and appearance of the bird: its skeletal structure, carriage, quantity of fluff and feather, length of leg and thigh which, when put together, gives us a bird which conforms to both shape and stance as determined by the standards laid down by the Pekin Club. How this shape or TYPE is achieved is often open to the individual breeder's opinion and belief over what features he considers should take precedence in the make-up of the Pekin. But the bird must conform to the standard.

The standard which now follows is reproduced by permission of the Pekin Club. This represents the 'blueprint' for the breed and each colour within that breed. One of the dangers in the fancy is that particular features may become exaggerated, so an overall balanced bird is no longer bred; this has to be guarded against.

THE STANDARD
GENERAL CHARACTERISTICS

CARRIAGE Bold, rather forward, the head to be lower than the tail giving necessary tilt.

TYPE Body short and broad. Back increasing in breadth to the saddle, which should be very full, rising well from between the shoulders and furnished with long, soft feathers. Breast deep and full. Wings short, tightly tucked up, the ends hidden by the saddle hackle. Tail short and full, soft without hard quill feathers, with abundant coverts almost hiding tail feathers, the whole forming one unbroken duplex curve with the back and saddle. Tail should be carried higher than the head; i.e. tilt.

HEAD Skull small and fine. Beak rather short, stout and slightly curved. Eyes large and bright.

Eyes red, orange or yellow, red preferred. In both sexes: beak yellow, but in dark colours may be shaded with black or horn. Comb: single, small, firm, perfectly straight and erect, well serrated, curved from front to back. Face smooth and fine, ear lobes smooth and fine, preferably nearly as long as the wattles, which are long, ample, smooth and rounded.

NECK Short, carried forward, with abundant long hackle reaching well down the back.

LEGS & FEET Legs and feet yellow. Legs short and well apart. Stout thighs hidden by plentiful fluff. Hocks completely covered with soft feathers curling round the joints, (stiff feathers forming "vulture hocks" are objectionable, but not a disqualification.) Shanks short and

Figure 3.1 Type is All Important

Figure 3.2 Pekin with Good Tilt

thick, abundantly covered with soft, outstanding feathers.
Toes: four, strong and straight, the middle and outer toes
plentifully covered with soft feathers to their tips.
PLUMAGE Very abundant, long and wide, quite soft
with very full fluff.

FEMALE   With the exception of the back, (rising to a
very full and round cushion,) the general characteristics
are similar to those of the male, allowing for the natural
sexual differences.

SUGGESTED WEIGHTS Male 24 – 28ozs. (680 – 790g.)
                                    Female 20 – 24ozs. (570 – 680g.)

CLUB STANDARD   Male not to exceed 24ozs
                                    Female not to exceed 20ozs.

SERIOUS DEFECTS FOR ALL COLOURS
Twisted or drooping combs.   Slipped or split wings.
Legs other than yellow, (except in blacks) Eyes other than
red, orange or yellow. Any deformity.

NOTES: When we look at a Pekin, we should see a soft,
globular shaped ball of fluff. The bird should sit low down,
though not so low that it appears to be squatting when still,
or creeping forward when in motion. The setting of the legs
in relation to the body is important. The shanks must be
sufficiently short in length to throw the frame of the bird
forward, so that its head appears to be lower than the tail.
This forward position is known in the Pekin fancy as "the

Figure 3.3 Note Length of Footings

Figure 3.4 Bird Standing Too High

tilt".

But no one body characteristic is dominant over all the others. The correct skeletal structure on its own is insufficient. The desired TYPE cannot be achieved unless the shaping of the bird by the quantity of fluff and broad feathers is such, that the Pekin appears to be rounded when viewed from any angle, but, copious amounts of fluff and feather alone will not necessarily produce a bird of good TYPE. All are interdependent.

Fluff, which appears low down the feather, next to the skin, is of the utmost importance for it is this which seems to give the basic bone structure its rounded shape before the required broad feathering sits over the top.

I am beginning to believe that perhaps, not enough attention is paid to the amount of fluff found on Pekins. Without copious amounts of dense fluff moulding thighs, breast and back, even birds which exhibit good, broad feathers, will fail to show that unbroken, soft, rounded shape that determines a good Pekin.

Interested in studying the feather development in the Pekin, I borrowed a pair of blacks and bred some chicks from them. I have retained one black pullet of excellent type, (she has won two major prizes already), but although her feathers are of excellent quality and beautifully broad, she does not have anywhere near as dense a layer of fluff as the lavender Pekins which were hatched at the same time.

The **breast** of the Pekin should be very broad, with the lower feathers long in length so as to give the impression that the lower edge of the bird is edged with a skirt. This, combined with a forward tilt, ensures that no hint of daylight can be seen through the legs.

The **saddle** of the Pekin should also be broad with a wide, full cushion rising out of the base of the hackle to form an unbroken curve. There should be no suggestion of the cushion being clipped in at the sides where it rises. Fluff at this point seems to be important in shaping the base of the cushion, being rather like the wadding or stuffing inside a chair, giving it shape, before the top covering, the feathers, finish off the whole. Legs and feet should also be well feathered, the feathering helping to form and mould the unbroken line of the body shape that is the challenge to achieve.

In conclusion, the aim when breeding Pekins, is to achieve an overall, rounded bird that has a forward tilt. TYPE always takes precedence over colour in any breeding programme. Remember, a beautifully feathered bird of excellent colour and precise markings, prepared and shown to perfection, will fail miserably if it fails on type.

Figure 3.5 A Trio Running on Grass

CHAPTER FOUR

SO, PEKINS ARE FOR YOU

Having made the decision to keep pekins, you should have already asked yourself the following questions.

1.   Have I sufficient time and enough real interest to care for my birds, day in, day out, regardless of the time of year or the weather?

Make no mistake, keeping poultry is both time consuming and demanding.   Seeing a pretty group of Pekins running on grass on a gentle summer's day is NOT the time to decide that keeping bantams is for you.   The real test of dedication is to have the ability to drag yourself out of bed to feed and clean out after a late night or when suffering from flu on a cold winter's morning in a gale force wind and driving rain.

2.   Have I sufficient room for the birds, either to be kept on grass or in pens indoors in intensive or semi-intensive conditions?

3.   Have I the ability to make good, sound draught free pens for my stock - or the money to pay others to perform the task?

A jumble of old boxes, roughly knocked together, which are ill-fitting and not waterproof will do neither the stock any good - nor your own reputation as a caring stockman.

4.   Why do I want to keep Pekins?

Your reasons for keeping them will help determine the kind of accommodation you will need to provide.

ACQUIRING YOUR STOCK

If you are able to provide satisfactory answers to these questions, just where and how do you go about looking for stock?

When choosing to keep any breed of poultry, whether large fowl or bantams, it is important that you first visit the local shows, either Agricultural Shows with a poultry section usually staged in a tent, or Poultry Club Shows often held in village halls during the showing season which is usually between September and February.

At these shows you can see the birds for yourself and most importantly, begin to know the breeders who are exhibiting them. You will not only begin to recognise who is a successful showman, but also, and most important of all, you will be able to judge for yourself which birds are shown in excellent health and condition. The successful stockman and breeder who takes pride in his birds, showing them in their best light, though not necessarily always winning, is the person you should approach for your stock. Dirty, unwashed, ill-prepared birds indicate owners who are themselves uncaring.

As a novice, it will be difficult for you to know just which breeders you can trust, as opposed to those who are out to sell their stock regardless of quality. Don't be afraid to ask questions. Find out who else the breeder you have chosen to buy from, has supplied with stock, talk to them and go and look at their stock.

Don't be carried away by the euphoria of becoming a poultry owner, and never buy on the spur of the moment. The bird that is being exhibited and takes your fancy, might

Figure 4.1 In Selecting Remember Type is Vital

Figure 4.2 A Drooping Comb is a Fault

well match up to the standards in colour and be of excellent type, but will not necessarily breed true. Take your time and select what you consider will best meet your requirements, making a mutually convenient arrangement to visit the breeder's premises. Then, you will be able to judge for yourself and assess the care taken of his birds away from the limelight of the showbench. Ask about the bloodline and discover how closely the birds are related. Be aware of the dangers of inbreeding. Continual inbreeding* may, over a period of time, intensify faults and affect the vigour of the stock.

Obviously, no breeder will be prepared to sell his coveted show birds, nor the inmates of his successful breeding pen, but a genuine, interested breeder, will be keen to promote the breed and guide the newcomer along the right lines, supplying stock, at a price, that will prove successful for you in the future and lay the foundations for your breeding programme. The golden rule on purchasing stock is that you should buy as good a bird as you can acquire, or afford, and, whichever colour you finally decide to keep, *remember that type is that most important consideration of all.*

If you are thinking of keeping Pekins for your own enjoyment and for the pleasure you will get from them when you see them running in the garden, then the birds you purchase might well have faults that would preclude them from the showbench or the breeding pen of the exhibitor/fancier. Perhaps the comb of the male is unevenly serrated, the head of a lavender a little too dark, or a buff uneven colour.

Inbreeding **and related matters on breeding require careful study and application so this general statement is only given on my experience with Pekins.**

These are faults in the Pekin that will lead the breeder to sell them at "pet price" and, providing that you are satisfied that the stock is healthy, they will give you years of enjoyment.

SELECTING STOCK FOR BREEDING

Perhaps the experiences Lee and Jessica Manion have had with their livestock, will lay the foundations for them as future breeders and exhibitors of Pekins. Certainly, many adults first acquire poultry "just for a few eggs", or " because we like to watch them in the garden," but, they become hooked and decide to breed Pekins themselves, determined to improve their stock.

If you do intend to become a serious breeder, then never, never buy inferior stock thinking that you will be able to breed good specimens from them. Only by buying the best within your means, will you be able to form a firm foundation on which to base your breeding programme and ultimately develop your own successful strain. It is far better to begin with a pair of good Pekins than a trio of inferior ones. Always be prepared to breed many from a few, rather than introduce poor quality females in the hope of obtaining a greater number of chicks.

TYPE is the most important consideration when buying stock. The previous chapter has, in some detail, dealt with what the Pekin fancy considers to be the ideal type and the features that contribute toward it. Remember that type is determined by:-

1. The bone structure of the bird, short shanks helping to promote a good tilt forward.

2. The carriage, which is influenced by the basic struc-

ture.

3.   **The fluff, which pads out and gives shape to the skeleton.**

4.   **The quality and quantity of the feathering.**

You will not be able to purchase the perfect bird, but you must be happy that it satisfies most of the criteria. Any faults in one bird in the breeding pen should be over-compensated for in the bird of the opposite sex, thus going some way in establishing a balance.

Now too, it is important to know the background history of the birds that you are about to buy. The showbird on the bench might appear sound in type and match up to the colour standards, but if other colours have been used in the breeding to achieve this excellence, the bird will be of little use in your breeding programme. Many a good buff Pekin has produced partridge or black progeny in subsequent matings, and the disappointed purchaser has therefore had to lose several breeding seasons before breeding out the undesired trait.

Generally, Pekins of good type can be relied upon to breed true, but some colours are more difficult than others. Black, white and mottled Pekins have been popular amongst the fancy for a very long time and consequently, shape in these is excellent. Buffs and lavenders are in a catch 22 situation. Their type is generally not good; they are difficult; few are ready to take them on; therefore they remain difficult.

Another important feature to consider when selecting breeding stock and one which is very often forgotten, is that of eye colour. Not only should the eye colour match the required standard, i.e. be large and bright, red, orange or yellow in colour, (though red is preferred,) but also, remember that the health of the bird is often reflected in their eyes.

Check also that both eyes are the same colour. One season I showed a male Pekin that passed several judges, as well as myself, until another exhibitor pointed out to me that one of the bird's eyes was red, but the other was green. Hold the bird up to face you, turning him to both sides to check both eyes. Never breed from a bird with green eyes or with poor eye colour. This is a defect which will be passed on to the progeny.

Another important often ignored feature is that of the **comb**. This should be evenly serrated, not twisted, drooping or showing side sprigs. Heavy, ugly combs lacking serrations, – usually at the back, should also exclude the bird from the breeding pen.

Today, too few breeders pay sufficient attention to the comb, and it seems to have presented problems forty years ago, when H. Easom Smith was worried that too many male Pekins had too small a comb. He suggested that, whilst combs should not show coarseness, fine serrations and small, smooth combs seemed to detract from their masculinity.

The best shaped male show bird may not necessarily be the most effective in the breeding pen. A cock with a broad, well rounded chest, may physically have problems in the act of mating, resulting in infertile eggs. Therefore, it might be better to select a male with a slightly cut away, though broad front and mate him with a female of good type, showing an especially well rounded breast. When putting together a

Ideal Comb

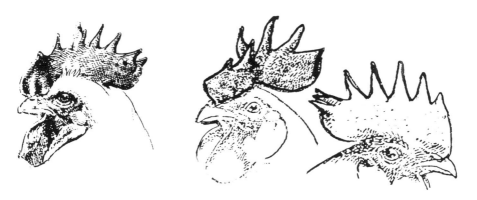

Side Sprigs Twisted Comb   Fish Tailed Comb

Faults in Comb

Figure 4.3 Examples of Combs

breeding pen, it is important to try to match birds which you hope will breed ideal specimens. Some suggest the correct approach is to over-compensate in one bird with any features that are lacking in the other, thereby balancing out slight faults in type or colour. The alternative approach is to breed from stock which has as many good features as possible in the hope that these will be passed to the progeny, but not using any birds with serious faults even if 'balancing' the two sides.

These are the most important basic factors to consider when putting together your breeding pen of Pekins, but other points need to be kept in mind depending upon which colour you are breeding. Some colours are undoubtedly easier to breed than others, when good results can be obtained from a single pen mating, whereas breeding colours such as partridge or barred call for some understanding of genetics and are really not colours for the novice. Further details about breeding the different colours can be found in the chapter on the colours of the Pekin.

If you decide that it is necessary to introduce fresh blood into your stock, if possible, go back to your original supplier and discuss your problems with him. It is generally regarded to be more satisfactory to introduce new blood on the female side, rather than the male. One female will produce one season's hatch of chicks, whereas a male will possibly be mated to several females. Should severe faults become obvious as a result of the new blood, providing that you have marked the chicks and kept records of the matings, only the progeny from that one female will need to be culled. Had faults appeared as a result of the introduction of a male bird,

many more chicks would have been affected and your breeding programme severely hindered.

Finally, theory and knowledge are important, but the
only way for the beginner to make progress, is to begin his
own breeding programme. Reading, talking and arguing are
no substitutes for practicalities. You will make mistakes,
but if you keep in mind what constitutes a good type and
breed only from the best you have, you will not go far wrong.

MAKING PROGRESS WITH YOUR BREEDING PROGRAMME

Having mated together your original birds and successfully hatched chicks, how do you progress from there?

First and foremost, if you are intending to become a
serious breeder, you must identify your eggs and the subsequent chicks, marking them and keeping detailed and accurate records. It is useless thinking that you will be able to
rely on memory in the future. As time passes and the chicks
grow away, there will be a high percentage of them that will
look much alike. Remember, they carry fifty per cent of the
characteristics of the father and fifty per cent of the characteristics of the mother, some of which will be bad faults as
well as good. Mark the chicks so that you know exactly
where they come from. Obviously a **one-to-one mating** is
easier to keep track of than a two or three to one.

Select your best males from the first year's hatch and
the best females and you are now ready to breed another
generation. But how to go about it?

INBREEDING

A simple explanation of inbreeding is that it involves the mating of birds that are very closely related; *for example,* brothers and sisters from your original mating. Remember again that the progeny will carry both the good and the bad characteristics already bred into their parents, so that mating brother and sister together might result in characteristics coming to the fore that would be better avoided, as well as the good points.

Sometimes, however, the method of inbreeding is used deliberately. The progeny from your first mating might include two excellent Pekins, sound in both type and colour, yet brother and sister in relationship. Mating them together this once is usually safe, as long as you select rigorously from the resulting progeny, cull poor stock and, the following year, revert to line breeding by mating a female back to her father and a male back to his mother. Continued inbreeding in an indiscriminate way will result in a gradual loss of vigour and deterioration of your stock, so it should not be used regularly in any breeding programme.

LINE BREEDING

This is the method used by most breeders to improve the quality of their stock by breeding within, and creating a family. The birds are mated back in direct line to their ancestors - sons mated back to their mothers and daughters mated back to their father. The progeny from these matings, are in turn, mated back to grandsire and grandma. This process can be continued for many generations without the need for the introduction of new blood.

Meticulous and accurate record keeping is imperative, with eggs and chicks marked and identified. Should you lose process can be continued for many generations without the need for the introduction of new blood. track of any bird within the family tree, discard it rather than risk breaking the chain through guesswork, otherwise all the work carried out before will be ruined and your breeding programme destroyed.

Only the very best birds should be used. Throughout your breeding programme type must be at the front of your mind. Be critical and look for faults and degeneration of your stock and be prepared to cull. However, don't be too hasty in your decisions over rejection. Pekins take a long time to reach maturity. Many a breeder will be able to tell the story of stock, given away as pets, developing into birds worthy of a first place in a major show.

Figure 4.4 Line Breeding -- Three Generations
Also see Figures 1.1 and 3.5.

CHAPTER FIVE

THE COLOURS

The Pekin Club of Great Britain recognises the following colours in the Pekin:

Barred	**Cuckoo**
Black	**Lavender**
Blue	**Mottled**
Buff	**Partridge**
Columbian	**White**

All other colours that are bred, such as Red and Birchen, are classed as *non-standard* colours and must be exhibited in the non-standard classes at poultry shows.

Some countries, America and Australia included, recognise many other colours in the Pekin as being standard and the novice fancier should exercise great care, ensuring that he refers only to the *British Standards* of the Pekin Club, if he wishes to exhibit in Britain.*

*It should be noted that the breed is referred to as Cochin in the USA and there are 16 colours and it is regarded as the most popular feathered leg bantam. Colours are Barred, Birchen, Black, Black-tailed Red, Blue, Brown Red, Buff, Buff Columbian, Columbian, Golden Laced, Mottled, Partridge, Red, Silver Laced, Silver Pencilled, and White. The general standard is much the same as the British.

THE NON-STANDARD COLOURS OF THE PEKIN.

The non-standard colours of the Pekin which are bred in this country, are kept by a minority of breeders who are interested in colour breeding programmes and who fully understand how the colours are derived and further developed. The non-standard classes are intended for breeders to exhibit birds which have been bred in a newly established colour. The breeding programme will have been continued over several years, before the birds of both sexes can be relied upon to breed true to the new colour and also match up to the required type. The classes are not intended for exhibitors to show a "sport", which has been bred by chance and cannot be reproduced.

Those who are interested in breeding new colours must, however, receive praise where it is due. It takes many years of dedicated work to produce a new standard and stable colour. Unwanted characteristics have to be eliminated, yet desired features, such as feathering on the feet and legs, for example, must be bred in. Eddie Starkey has already been involved in a programme for four years in an attempt to revive the beautifully coloured silver partridge Pekin, and still has a long way to go before he will be satisfied with his work. Yet, he has made great progress so his patience is proving to be worthwhile.

For the majority of Pekin fanciers, however, the standard colours provide more than enough of a challenge and many argue that there will be time in the future to breed and develop new colours, when the present colours have all reached a high and acceptable standard. They argue that already within the breed, type has too often been sacrificed

for colour. Undoubtedly, many of the colours are very difficult to breed to type and, as Eddie Starkey argues:

**"Until more are prepared to take on a colour, stick to it
and not give up when the end results seem a long way
away."**

He also stresses the fact that some, such as Buffs and
Lavenders, will take many years of breeding to reach the
degree of perfection of the blacks and the whites. However,
one breeder, Peter Hinton, has recently won major awards
with these two difficult colours.

Generally though, too many birds fail on both type and
quality of feather in the quest for the perfect colour and
markings. Some colours, such as the Barred, are almost
non-existent, with few if any entries some years at the two
major shows. Often breeders are unclear about the markings
demanded, confusing the Cuckoo markings with those of the
Barred, so that both colours are frequently to be found in
both classes.

Because the majority of breeders over the years have
kept and developed the Black and White Pekin, both colours
are able to provide outstanding examples in both type and
feather quality, and generally, can be relied upon to breed
true to type. Consequently, entries in these classes at the
shows are large. Birds in other colours have been sold to
several black and white enthusiasts who initially showed
interest, yet few birds have appeared on the show bench in
the following years. In comparison with the safer black or
white Pekin, a coloured bird has proved too great a challenge

and, consequently, breeding programmes have been abandoned.

WHICH COLOUR IS FOR YOU?

Having discovered that Pekins really are the birds you want to keep, you will have little difficulty in choosing a colour to suit you for they are available, in this country, in ten colours.

However, your final decision is likely to be influenced by two factors;

1.   **Why you want to keep Pekins**
2.   **How you intend to house them.**

If your intention is to keep them solely for enjoyment, then you are fortunate, for you can satisfy your own personal choice and purchase whichever colour appeals to you. If you do not mind your white or lavender Pekins turning a brassy yellow when exposed to the sun, or your buffs losing their strong colour and fading, then the full range of colours is available for your choice. But if you want white whites and pale, silvery, even-coloured lavenders, your birds must live away from the direct sunlight. Immediately then, the facilities you have available in which to house your Pekins, will play a part in determining which colours you decide to keep. However, some colours are more complicated to breed than others and would be better left until you have gained some knowledge and experience.

Finally, before you make your choice, remember that the following points must be kept in mind.

1.   **Type**
2.   **Quality of feather.**
3.   **Colour.**

BARRED

> **COLOUR STANDARD**   Each feather barred across
> with black bands, having a beetle green sheen on
> a white background. The bands or barring to be
> of equal proportion - black and white. Barring
> should continue through the shaft and into the
> under fluff, and each feather must finish with a
> black tip. Plumage should present a bluish, steely
> appearance free from brassiness and of a uniform
> shade throughout. Legs and feet yellow. Eyes red/
> orange.

Too often the markings of the Barred Pekin are confused with those of the Cuckoo, and vice versa. Like the
Barred Rock, from where the colour originates, the background colour to the barring in the Pekin, should be white.
Breeders should not be confused if they keep this in mind for
the background colour in the Cuckoo is supposed to be light
French-grey.

Double mating is necessary when breeding the Barred
Pekin, so once again you will be virtually breeding two colours if you are aiming to achieve exhibition standard birds of
both sexes. The black barring on the white ground should be
striped straight across each feather and not in a V shape.
Intelligent selective breeding is necessary when keeping the
Barred, for it is a difficult colour to achieve and preserve
which is why the colour is almost extinct. Fortunately, one
or two breeders are attempting to recreate the colour by
crossing the Barred Rock with the Black Pekin, but it will be
several years before the results of their work is in evidence
on the showbench.

BLACK

> **COLOUR STANDARD**   Rich sound black with lustrous beetle green sheen throughout, free from white or coloured feathers.   Some light undercolour in adult males is permissible so long as it does not show through.   Dark legs are permissible if the soles of the feet and backs of shanks are yellow.

Black Pekins are the most popular colour and classes at both major and local shows are always very well supported.   They are obviously easier to keep clean than the lighter colours, and exhibitors do not have problems with soiled and badly stained footings.   The feathers are not affected by sunlight and, indeed, many breeders believe that a light shower of rain is recommended for improving the sheen on the feathers.

As blacks have been bred for many years, there is rarely difficulty in producing birds of excellent type and feather quality, providing that good breeding stock is used. The challenge with the Black Pekin is to breed a bird which combines rounded shape, breadth in keel and cushion, a good tilt forward and sound, black colour which goes right down through the feathers.

Light undercolour in the cock bird is allowed, but the female should be solid black in colour all through, with the top feathers exhibiting a good beetle green sheen.   There must be no confusion between a green sheen and one which shows blue in colour.   The latter is not acceptable and would be deemed a fault on the show bench.

Cock birds used in the breeding pen must always be of a good type, showing tilt, with a broad breast, short back and high rise to form a wide cushion. Length and breadth of feather is important. Male birds that have some light in their undercolour will usually produce sound, black females.

The female in the breeding pen, must be black right through to the ends of the feathers down into the fluff. Avoid using birds that are sooty in colour and if your stock are beginning to show signs of sootiness, it might perhaps, be an indication that fresh blood should be introduced. It is usually advisable to introduce new stock on the female side. Like the male, the females should be of good type and as broad and round as possible, giving an overall impression of softness. Once again, length of feather is important, with the tips being broad and rounded.

In both the male and the female, heavily feathered thighs with ample fluff will usually mean that the breeder will not have a problem with lack of feathering on the feet where length of feather is more important than the amount.

Figure 5.1 Show Day
This will indicate whether you have the correct type & colour

Figure 5.2 Black Female Owned by the Author.

BLUE

> **COLOUR STANDARD**   A rich, pale pigeon blue,
> free from lacing, but with rich, dark blue hackles
> in the back and tail of the male.

Blue Pekins are not a colour recommended for the novice breeder for it is very difficult to breed birds that are free from lacing. To produce good, exhibition birds of both sexes two pens are needed, as they are when breeding the partridge colour, so, once again, if it is your intention to breed blues, you are virtually keeping two colours if your aim is to breed both cockerels and pullets of exhibition quality.

Some basic knowledge of genetics is advisable and a full understanding of the make-up of the blue colour is imperative. The blue colour is derived from a fusing of black and white. Breeding together black and white will produce some blacks, some whites and some birds which will be splashed. By mating the splashed progeny back to the black progeny you will again produce a mixture of colours, but this time you should get some blues.

You will need patience, for it will take several years to produce your own strain of good coloured Blue Pekins, but it is well worth the challenge. The splashed birds that are bred, providing that they are of good type, are invaluable in the breeding programme. When mated to blue they can be used to lighten the colour, or, if your birds tend to be too pale in colour, a black bred male mated to a blue female will darken the feathering. The sound blue shade must be carried right down the feather and into the fluff and must be free of lacing.

The feather quality of the Blue Pekin is usually very fine indeed, originating as it does from the black and white. The feathers are usually long in length and very broad at the tips. Birds without these qualities should not be used in the breeding pens unless type and colour are both outstanding.

BUFF

COLOUR STANDARD   Sound buff of a perfectly even shade throughout, quite sound to the roots of the feathers, and free from black, white or bronze feathers. The exact shade of buff is not material so long as it is level throughout and free from shaftiness, mealiness or lacing.

Buff is the colour of the original Pekins first brought to England in the 1860's. They are, however, very difficult to breed true to type and, disheartened by their results, many breeders have shied away from this colour, preferring the more reliable black and whites. There are a few dedicated breeders of buffs, who have supplied good breeding stock to others in an attempt to promote the colour and to encourage others to take up the challenge. However, few birds from these new breeders have subsequently appeared on the show-bench. It is only by more taking up the colour and striving to improve the type, that progress will ever be made in the right direction. That it can be done is evident by the success of the breeder, Peter Hinton, whose buff Pekin female won the Club Championship at Newbury in recent times.

Once again, the basic rule must be to breed only from birds that are of good type. Birds that are narrow across the breast and leggy, that have long backs, should be rejected from the breeding pen, no matter how perfect the colour of the feathers. Generally, it is the males that stand too high with daylight showing between their legs, whereas the females do seem broader and rounder in appearance.

The standard states that the colour should be "an even shade of buff throughout," but the exact colour required is open to misinterpretation. Having selected your two birds for breeding, both exhibiting good type, the actual colour of the birds must be secondary to the evenness of the shade which must continue right through the feather into the fluff. Variations in the undercolour are common, the chief fault being a much lighter undercolour. If it is streaked with black or white, the breeding of the parent stock might need to be questioned, as blacks or whites might have been used in the breeding to either lighten or darken the shade, or, to improve feather quality.

Careful selection of birds and intelligent breeding will result in the gradual evolution of a good, even shade of buff as you build up your own strain. Do not use birds that are uneven in colour in the breeding pen, avoiding those that show red on the hackle or saddle as well as the already mentioned flecking in the undercolour.

Several years ago, a breeder, John McNeil, imported buffs from America in an attempt to improve the British Stock. Both the colour and the feathering in these birds were superior to the British buffs being bred at the time, but they failed miserably on type and size, being too large and standing high.

Balance in the breeding pen is very important. Be
critical, look for colour faults in the male and try to balance
these out by overcompensating in the female. Buff Pekins
are very beautiful birds. Hopefully, in time, more breeders
will show interest in this colour and breed them to the standard achieved in the blacks and whites.

COLUMBIAN

COLOUR STANDARD   Pearl white with black
markings. Head and neck hackle white with dense
black stripe down middle of each feather, free
from black edgings, or black tips. Saddle pearl
white. Tail feathers and tail coverts glossy green
black, the coverts laced or not with white. Primaries black, or black edged with white. Secondaries black on inner edge, white outer. Remain-
der of plumage entirely white of pearl-grey shade,
free from ticking. Undercolour, either slate, blue-
white or white.

Although Columbian Pekins are bred by only a few
breeders in this country, they are certainly eye-catching and
their beautiful colouring is bound to attract many more in
the fancy and increase their popularity. Originally bred from
a Pekin and Sussex mating, double mating is necessary to
produce exhibition standard males and females and balance
of colouring when selecting breeding stock is of utmost importance. The body colour should be pure white, contrasting
sharply with the black feathers which should show a glossy
green sheen. Unfortunately, as with some of the other, more

difficult colours of the Pekin, in attempting to perfect the colour, breeders have often sacrificed shape and type.

CUCKOO

COLOUR STANDARD **Evenly barred with dark slate on light French-grey ground.**

Like the Buffs, the Cuckoo Pekin was originally imported from China. Unfortunately, the first hen died and in an attempt to preserve the colour, the cock bird was, in turn, mated to a Black; a greyish white; and a Barred Rock Bantam and eventually, the cuckoo colour was re-introduced. The birds became firm favourites with the fancy. However, fashion is fickle and their popularity died and in an attempt to once again revive the colour, matings were made between the Barred Rock Bantam and the Black Pekin.

A project using the cross was undertaken by Wilf Jackson and Brian Carlos during the late sixties. However, they were far from satisfied with their results, the birds being too narrow. Through the local grapevine they discovered that other fanciers had been working on a similar project, but, being from the Yorkshire contingent they kept their work very close to their chests.

Brian Carlos writes, "I found myself penetrating deep into Yorkshire with a hit list of three fanciers. Aware that if I mentioned my interest in Cuckoos I would get nowhere, I adopted standard tactics. I took the kids along for the soft touch; did not admit connections with any known fancier and remained aware that some sheds would not be for my eyes.

The first two establishments revealed no traces of experimental breeding, so I pushed my deteriorating, though trusty A35 a little further to the premises of Mr Bruce Dixon. I explained that my visit was social, but that I might be interested in a black pullet. I struck gold. Running loose were several cuckoo type cockerels. I left some time later with one of the desired birds in a box "a pet for one of the children!"

However, on inspection, both Wilf and Brian had to agree that the Yorkshire project was no further on than their own. Something was needed to provide the breadth that was lacking in their "made Cuckoo." It was there in their own backyard. A Maran Bantam hen was introduced into the breeding programme and success followed within two years.

Cuckoos are often confused with the Barred Pekin and even at exhibition standard, fanciers are unclear about the markings and birds of each colour pattern are often exhibited in the one class. There should be no need for this confusion, for the background colours are different, and the barring on the Barred Pekin a very obvious horizontal, black stripe.

Cuckoo Pekins can be bred from straightforward Cuckoo/Cuckoo matings, but gradually, over a period of time, the Cuckoo colouring darkens and the desired french-grey background is lost. The barring also becomes indistinct and blurred, with the background colour fusing into the barring until eventually, the barring is lost altogether. The colour must be revived and breeders introduce black into the breeding pen. The resulting progeny should consist of some well marked Cuckoo chicks and some Blacks and providing the latter are good type, they can be used in the Cuckoo breeding programme.

The barring around the neck and the breast should appear in concentric circles and throughout, the cuckoo pattern should continue right through the feather and down into the skin. Too often, birds are bred with the barring visible only a short way down the feather, instead of right through the length and into the fluff.

Breeding the Cuckoo Pekin is exciting and challenging for you never know just how the colour will turn out; if there will be good clear barring; or if the background colour will be the desired french-grey.

LAVENDER

COLOUR STANDARD   The lavender is not a lighter shade of the Blue Pekin.   It is different genetically and is of a lighter, more silver tint without the darker shade associated with the normal blue.   The silver tint is most obvious in the neck and saddle hackle feathers of the male. Beak yellow or horn. Eyes red, orange or yellow. Legs and toes deep yellow.

When I write, the Lavender Pekin is the most beautiful of all the colours, I have to admit that I am biased, as this is the colour that I breed myself.

The difficulty, and therefore the challenge with the Lavender Pekin, is to breed a small bird, true to type, of a pale, silvery lavender shade which is even in colour throughout. This colour should be carried right through the feathering and into the fluff.

Many lavenders seen today, are streaked with dark blue or grey and the majority have dark heads and neck hackles, all faults to be avoided.

It is very difficult to breed a lavender which shows both good type and even, light colour. The feathers of the lavender Pekin are short in comparison with most of the other colours, especially in the region of the lower breast, where length of skirt is so important in helping to create the overall impression of a bird with a good tilt, that is, the head of the bird being lower than its tail. Without this skirt hiding daylight between the legs, a throw forward as the result of skeletal structure, will not necessarily result in a bird that appears to have the required tilt, when it is compared with a bird that has long breast feathers.

Some breeders may disagree with my views on the importance of the skirt feathers, arguing that a bird will only show the tilt if the bone structure allows this, but I firmly believe that if the bird is lacking in long feathering in this region, no matter how broad it is in the keel, or how short it is in the shank, the bird, when viewed from the front will still appear to be slightly off the ground.

However, when compared with many of the other colours of the Pekin, the lavender does seem to have a greater abundance of fluff. Given, therefore, that the skeleton of the bird is such that the head is lower than the tail, the fluff which helps to determine the rounded shape and padding of the Pekin, if covered with long, broad feathers similar to those found in other colours, must be a very important factor in breeding a bird which is of good type. If the lavender is to

Figure 5.3 Lavender Male Bred by Author

Figure 5.4 Lavender Female Bred by Author

be bred to the same high standard as blacks and whites, work must be carried out on improving the feather quality.

The tail feathers of the male lavender Pekin often resemble the narrow tendrils of feather found in the Silkie, instead of the long, broad, curling feathers that should make up the cushion.

As with the buff Pekin, John McNeil introduced lavenders from America into the British breeding programme, but once again these birds were too leggy and too large, although of superior feather quality. Several years ago, here in Cornwall, Ellis Penegegan and Peter Odgers purchased a pair of lavender Pekins whilst at the Reading Show. The birds had been imported from Holland, and as the asking price was £100, they bought the birds between them. Although the birds were small in size and of reasonable type, they were much too dark in colour.

Often, breeders have introduced black or blue into the breeding pen in an attempt to improve the feathering, but in doing so, have either darkened the desired light colour, increasing the amount of streaking and ticking in the birds, or, when blue has been used, the feathers do seem to show signs of lacing.

When selecting birds for the breeding pen, I look for type first and foremost, with evenness, in a pale, silvery colour coming second. If I have a female that is a little on the dark side, though evenly coloured without an over dark head, provided that she is of outstanding type, I will use her with a very light male, thus balancing out the colour.

I am very selective over which stock I retain for showing and breeding, rejecting any that are too narrow, stand too high, have poor combs or show blue in the head or the hackle. My best show male is not necessarily used in the breeding pen, for I have found that a bird with too much chest, may have difficulty in mating.

I follow a line breeding programme, mating females back to fathers and grandfathers and males back to mothers and grandmothers. All my eggs, chicks and adults are marked and records kept. I am already able to see a family likeness on the male side, with improvements in both comb and length of back in my youngest male.

Figure 5.5 Mottled Male owned by Clive Stephens

MOTTLED

COLOUR STANDARD   Evenly mottled with white at the tip of each feather on a rich black with beetle-green sheen.

Mottled Pekins, once known as Black Spangled Pekins, have been popular since the 1930's. Providing that stock of good type is used in the breeding pen, they can be relied upon to breed true to type, and usually have long feathers of excellent quality.

The challenge of the Mottled Pekin is to produce a bird whose feathers are correctly marked with white which, to quote the colour standard, should be tipped on the end "of each feather." The easiest way to describe the ideal marking pattern, is to compare it with the feathering found on the Ancona - a black bird with a good green sheen, having each feather tipped with white, the tipping or mottling as we know it on the Pekin, being as evenly distributed as possible.

I keep Anconas, so I am very aware of the difficulty in achieving the V-shaped tipping at the end of each feather. I always compare the feather and its tipping with that of a finger with its nail, and even allowing for the generous amount and length of feather in the Pekin, I have yet to see what I would call good mottling. Type in the birds exhibited is excellent, as is the quality of the feathering, yet, too many birds are shown with very little white in the tips. The males, in particular, too often have feathers that are fully white, especially in the footings, yet they pass as mottled.   The females do seem to be more evenly tipped, yet the contrast in colour between the black and the white is often indistinct

Figure 5.6 Buff Hen with Low Carriage

Figure 5.7 Barred Hen
Bird has a rather upright stance and body is not rounded enough.

and smudged.

In the early days of the colour, mottles were bred by mating a spangled, (mottled) bird to black Pekins, but today, they can be successfully bred from a mottled/mottled mating, although sometimes a black bird is introduced to maintain the beetle-green sheen. Following moulting, they do seem to lighten out each year, with the white spreading further down the feather, giving the bird a look described as "gay," rendering it unsuitable for exhibiting again.

PARTRIDGE

COLOUR STANDARD   MALE   Head dark orange red, neck hackle bright orange or golden red, becoming lighter towards the shoulders and preferably shading off to as near lemon colour as possible, each feather distinctly striped down the middle with black, and free from shaftiness, black tipping or black fringe. Saddle hackle to resemble neck hackle as nearly as possible. Breast, thighs and under-parts, tail coverts, wing butts, foot feathers, hock feathers and fluff, a lustrous green-black, free from grey, rust or white. Back, shoulder coverts and wing bow, rich crimson. Primaries, black, free from white or grizzle.   Secondaries, black inner web, bay outer, showing a distinct wing bay when closed.

PARTRIDGE (Cont.)

> COLOUR STANDARD FEMALE Head and hackle
> light gold or straw, each feather distinctly striped
> down the middle with black. Remainder a clear
> light partridge brown, finely and evenly pencilled
> all over with concentric rings of dark shade,
> (preferably glossy green black). The whole of the
> uniform shade frequently described as the colour
> of a dead oak leaf, with three concentric rings of
> pencilling, or more over as much of the plumage
> as possible.

If you decide to breed partridge Pekins, you must understand from the beginning, that if your intention is to produce birds of exhibition quality in colour of *both sexes* you must breed each sex in a distinct pen. The intricate and complicated markings required on both the male and the female, cannot be obtained merely by mating together two birds of exhibition quality in the one pen.

In order to achieve the Partridge colour standard in exhibition males, the females used will be very different in colouring from the exhibition female. In a similar way, to achieve good exhibition females, the male used in the breeding pen should not be of the sound colour required in an exhibition male.

You can see that two pens must be used (known as *Double Mating*) if you are to breed well marked examples of the two sexes.

It is also very important, and indeed, necessary, for the intending breeder of the Partridge colour to be very clear about the colour standard required, in other words, be sure about the ultimate goal. Your ability to select birds of the right mix, will determine whether or not in the end you are successful.

Breeding Partridge Pekins is not a task for the novice, for even if you mate together two birds of the "right mix", you cannot guarantee the result. If it were as easy as that, the perfect bird would have been bred years ago. Be prepared to talk to breeders familiar with the partridge colour and ask their advice.

To produce quality exhibition males, the male bird should conform as near as possible to the colour standard and be paired to a female who in colour, is **not** like the exhibition female. She should **not** show signs of clear, concentric pencilling, but should have indistinct pencilling on the body, lemon coloured hackles with solid black striping, deep ground colour and good beetle-green sheen where ever possible – i.e., she shows signs of the male colour characteristics.

To produce good quality exhibition pullets, the female bird should be as near perfect in colouring as possible, whilst the male should show signs of gold pencilling, have a broken coloured black breast showing red-rust, and have a top colour which is generally darker than that of the cock breeder – ie., he shows signs of the female colour characteristics.

To simplify, what you are doing is mating together birds, one conforming as near as possible to the colour standard, and the other showing some of the colour characteristics of the same sex.

Before purchasing a pullet breeding male, it is important to check parentage to ensure that he really is pullet bred. He might show the signs in colouring of being a pullet breeder, but in fact, he might be a mis-marked exhibition male and would therefore be useless to breed good pullets.

The skill in selecting your birds is to balance the colour mix between the sexes and hopefully, produce some chicks with good, clear markings. You must be prepared to accept that there will be a large number of chicks which will fail on type, colour or both, so the wastage is great. Type must take precedence over colour. Time and patience are the great essentials. The partridge colour is a challenge, but very worthwhile. They are beautiful birds and the colour well deserves the name awarded to it, "The Royalty of the Showpen"

WHITE

COLOUR STANDARD   Pure snow-white, free from cream or yellow tinge, or black splashes or peppering.   Comb, face and wattles and ear lobes, bright red.

The white Pekin, is one of the most popular of the colours and consequently, breeders have developed a bird that is reliable in breeding true to type. Like the black Pekin, the feathers are long and of excellent quality.

The challenge of the white Pekin is to be able to breed a bird that is rounded in shape, gives an impression of softness, especially in the female, is broad in the breast and the cushion, has long and broadly tipped feathers, and, is a sound, clear white in colour.

Intelligent, selective breeding will ensure that the white of the feathers does not show a brassy, yellow tinge, a

Figure 5.8 Columbian Female
Colour pattern found in other breeds,eg; Brahmas & Light Sussex

Figure 5.9 White Female. Owned by Clive Stephens

very common fault found in the white Pekin. If whites are exposed to the sun, the feathers do become brassy, but this is not caused by the breeding. If you are lucky, your birds will lose all this discolouration from exposure, when they moult out.

When choosing your pen for breeding, select only those birds that are pure in white colour – any yellowing in the feathers will be reflected in the progeny. Always use birds of the cleanest colour. Often, brassiness is more apparent in the male bird, but if the male has to be used regardless, ensure that the female used with him, is of the purest white and free of any yellow tinges.

It is important to remember that the original Pekins were buff in colour and that the other colours were "created" from outcrossing with both other breeds and other colours of Pekin and therefore it is still feasible that a recessive gene will show through.

Once again, it is important to know the background history of your breeding stock and to purchase your breeding pairs from a fancier who has not introduced another colour into his Pekins. It is generally accepted that whiteness can be restored, should your stock show signs of losing their clarity of colour, by using a black bird in the breeding pen. However, by eliminating one fault, you may be introducing others and if you do introduce a different colour into your stock, you must be prepared for the colour to right itself. The unwanted gene could lie dormant for several generations and then suddenly come to light once again, producing black feathers and smuttiness in the colouring.

Figure 6.1 A Ready Made Ark

Figure 6.2 Raised Pens are Suitable for Elderly or
Disabled Fanciers

CHAPTER SIX

GENERAL MANAGEMENT OF PEKINS

HOUSING

In spite of their small size and short, heavily feathered legs, Pekins are surprisingly active little birds, although they are nowhere near as flighty as breeds such as Leghorns and Anconas. As with all types of poultry, breed characteristics such as flightiness will help determine the kind of housing most suitable for them.

Pekins are busy little birds, appearing to gain great pleasure from being given sufficient room to waddle about and scratch their way around in small runs, yet, they are equally happy when kept in more confined accommodation.

However, this does not mean that they should be forced to spend their days solely in small pens, such as the type and size of those used for showing, but, where the fancier has limited space, they are a breed eminently suited to more intensive conditions. Many fanciers are not fortunate in having a garden with a grassed area. Their birds will live inside, and, provided that the penning supplied is sufficiently spacious, Pekins will live happily in this way for many years.

Fanciers who choose to keep and show the colours such as white, lavender or buff, must keep their show stock out of the sunlight, so it is imperative that their birds are housed inside.

Before describing in greater detail, the kinds of housing that may be provided, it is perhaps relevant to discuss here the argument, often voiced, over the pros and cons of chicken being given "freedom." To many "freedom" in this context represents a large, unfenced, grassy area where birds are able to roam at will, returning only to the chicken house for food, water and protection at night. These same people who profess to care about the welfare of chicken do not understand the real danger that the birds face from predators.

In my own area, should our bantams be given complete freedom, their lives, even those of my flighty Anconas, would come to an abrupt and very untimely end within a week. Foxes visit us in broad daylight, and although, thankfully we are not troubled by dogs, neighbourhood cats seem determined to stalk, attack and catch anything with feathers that moves. Our local doctor has recently lost his entire stock of poultry, including a broody contentedly sitting on eggs, during daylight hours.

Foxes are now urbanised and so accustomed to human life, that they are prepared to come into gardens by day. Our local primary school was delighted that a vixen had made her home and reared two cubs on the corner of the school playing field, yet had to come to terms with the loss of pet rabbits and chicken by the residents whose gardens bordered the school.

Keeping animals is heavily linked with responsibility. It is unfair to blame the fox- he is following his natural instincts. It is our responsibility to protect our poultry from not only the fox, but also from other predators, such as the mink in some regions of the country. If we fail, then we must forgive the fox for taking advantage of his easy pickings.

IDEAS FOR HOUSING PEKINS

If you are starting from scratch, it is advisable to pause, and think about your needs and the space you have available. Also, be very clear about your aims, not just for the present, but for your longterm hobby. Whether you buy ready made units, or intend to construct your own, cost is all important. Your aim should be to provide housing that is multi-purpose, in otherwords, it can be adapted and used during the complete cycle of the poultry year. Then, you will really be getting the maximum out of your outlay and, have real value for money.

If your intention is to keep just a few Pekins to look at and enjoy, then a portable arc, or house and run combined would be ideal. They can be purchased ready made, at a price, or be constructed at home from exterior weather board, and should be sufficiently light in weight to be moved onto fresh ground every three days or so.

However, if your grass is limited, or if you want to breed Pekins for showing, indoor, covered accommodation is essential. Ingenuity is needed to provide a suitable living environment for your birds, without compromising your own garden.

Sheds, outhouses, or wash-houses can all be fitted with units and runs for your birds. For those with just a small backyard, the surrounding walls can be used to attach pens and runs, although these must be given adequate protection from extremes in the weather. Positioned at hip height, units such as these are accessible to wheelchairs, providing a very special interest for anyone who is disabled or of limited mobility. I have seen a garden chalet converted in this way, the pens raised so that the fancier in the wheelchair can move up close to the units, so enabling him to handle the birds and clean out and feed with comparative ease. The double doors of the chalet remain open all day, so that the birds have maximum light and ventilation, yet are protected from sun, wind and rain. Also, the neighbours in this urban area, are visually well satisfied by a well maintained and aesthetically pleasing garden chalet.

Whether you choose to house your Pekins indoors, or out, certain basic rules must be observed. Adequate ventilation must be provided both day and night, free from draughts waterproof and, fully protected from extreme conditions of rain, wind and sun. Lighting, whether natural or artificial is of paramount importance for it controls the correct functioning of the bird's glands which in turn, affect growth and subsequent egg production.

A PERSONAL APPROACH TO HOUSING PEKINS.

As we keep mainly lavender Pekins, we try to provide a variety of housing units for our birds which are all multipupose and therefore used according to the time of the year, that is whether it is the breeding, rearing or showing season. Keeping the costs down is a high priority, with pens and runs constructed in such a way that they can be simply adapted to fill any need.

As an example, show pens are made in block form, so that when room is required for brooders within reach of electric points, they can be moved to the far end of the shed and used for small numbers of growing stock which no longer require heat. In turn, the brooder boxes can be placed on their sides when no longer required for chicks, and used to accommodate one or two adult birds.

OUTSIDE.

All our breeding stock spend the greater part of their lives outside, on grass. As they are no longer involved with the showbench, it doesn't matter if their footings become dirty or if their feathers become bronzed by the sun. We move inside only when the weather deteriorates, partly through choice for we are fortunate in having space under cover, and partly, because our site is very open and exposed to the south westerly gales which sweep in from the sea. Once the weather settles in the spring, our Pekins are again put out on grass.

Our outside units are all run and pen combined and have been home constructed from either exterior sterling board or shuttering ply. Over time, my husband has improved on his original Mark 1 model, until now, Mark 6 seems to incorporate all our needs. Measuring around 2'6" (76cm) in width and 5' (152cm) in length, the covered house area has a waterproof, hinged lid which slopes backwards to ensure that the water drains away from the run, and gives easy access for cleaning out and collecting eggs. An even more refined and improved model could include an exterior nest box, but we haven't found this necessary and, having no projections, stacking and storing in the winter months is a simple process.

The mesh covered run area also includes a mesh floor to prevent predators from burrowing underneath and it serves to keep feathered feet off the grass, very important in prolonged spells of hot weather. We have surplus sheets of board available to cover the tops of the runs should the weather demand it. The pophole is worked by a paddle and is fitted to operate from the same side as the door which gives access into the run area. We have found this feature to be a necessity. When wishing to shut in stock on light summer evenings, they can be shepherded into the house with one hand, whilst the other is free to operate the paddle. A worthwhile tip is to train your birds to go into the house when they can see a cane poked through the mesh of the run. I use a white, plastic garden cane and now I have no trouble in encouraging them inside without resorting to bribery with corn. There were times, in the past, when we longed for an early night, but couldn't go to bed on the daylight evenings, (or go out) as the chicken were still wide awake, and active in their runs.

Keeping in mind that all our units are multi-purpose, we have made the popholes especially large, both in width and height. This means that our Pekin units can be used as conditioning Pens between shows, by our long-tailed Bantam Sumatra Game, with no damage to their flowing tails as they pass in and out of the pophole.

These portable units are lightweight and can easily be managed by one person by shifting one end at a time onto the fresh grass. There are two carrying handles at each end which facilitates transportation over a greater distances. Many retired couples have written to me of the enjoyment they gain from the Pekins, so weight of house and run are an important consideration as you become less active. Similarly, these units can be easily managed by a child.

Figure 6.3 Mark 6 Accommodation

Figure 6.4 P. H. Q.

INSIDE

Inside accommodation for our Pekin stock is provided by two garden sheds.

Our first shed, measuring 6' (183cm) by 4' (122cm) was known in the early days, when I had only one pair of lavender Pekins, as P.H.Q., or Pekin Headquarters. Now that we have more stock, it has been fitted out with three pens, each large enough to house a pair or a trio, and three others, suitable for a pair or a single bird. The lower pens are protected from droppings and soiling from above, by the provision of a four inch overhang between the stacking layers. All units are painted once a year with white paint to facilitate cleaning and to deter parasites. Using white paint rather than stain, means that the house and the pens always look bright, clean and cheerful.

During the warmer months the glass in the windows is replaced by mesh to give maximum ventilation both day and night, and in our war against foxes, we have fitted double, ranch-style doors of mesh inside the original solid door, which remains open all day. During the winter months, the mesh in the double doors is covered with clear polythene to keep out the wind and rain, yet allow in maximum daylight.

If the sun is particularly strong in summer, these doors are covered with old net curtaining to protect the pale lavender feathers, and to date, no birds kept in P.H.Q. have been adversely affected.

The second shed is much larger, measuring 16' (488cm) by 8' (244cm) and is within easy reach of electricity. This is fitted in such a way, that it is multi purpose with most of the units being interchangeable depending upon the need and the time of the year.

At the far end, the width has been divided into three pens, measuring 2'7" (79cm) wide by 4' (122cm) deep with storage space over the top for show baskets and boxes. These pens are in use all year round, as breeding pens for trios, or accommodation for growing stock. One pen has recently been fitted with a box unit on the back wall some twenty two inches off the ground, where on a rotating basis, a cock bird can be housed, thus utilising previously wasted space. The other two pens are soon to receive similar overhead units.

These pens are divided by wire mesh, with six inch boards along the bottom to deter cock birds from fighting and pecking between pens.

Down one length of the shed, a unit, originally the shell of a wardrobe, has been constructed providing seven pens for single and one double for two or more. There is storage space underneath for small items, but all the pens are positioned above, or at waist level to eliminate bending. There is also room along this side of the shed for brooder boxes during the breeding season, once again placed at waist level.

The full length of the other side of the shed is fitted with a workbench. There is room underneath for the plastic dustbins used to store feedstuffs, enabling them to be pushed well back, creating a wide gangway for access, Above, on the workbench, show pens constructed in block form are fitted during the show season and are replaced with brooder boxes or box and run during the chick rearing time. These show pens are extra large in size, so that an adult bird could live quite happily in one for some time. Because the pens have been made in individual units or modules, they are easy to stack and store when not in use.

Everything has to be available for use throughout the year, so good maintenance and cleanliness are very important. Run and floor sides, show pens, chick boxes and brooders are given a coat of white paint each year at "spring cleaning time." depending upon when they are free of stock. Nothing is ever stored or left unused in a dirty condition. When birds are kept indoors in close proximity, cleanliness is vital, so scrubbing out and disinfecting is part of the normal routine in the management of my Pekins.

All outside runs and houses as well as the two Pekin sheds, are given an annual coat of wood preservative. Not only does this lengthen their lives, but it uniforms the overall look of the Bantam accommodation, and prevents the garden from resembling Steptoe's Junk Yard.

ACCOMMODATION FOR CHICKS AND GROWING STOCK

Chicks hatched in an incubator, should not be removed until they are thoroughly dried out. I usually like to leave them about ten hours or overnight, before placing them in their homemade brooder.

Our brooders are wooden boxes which are a minimum of fourteen inches (36cm) deep and are covered by a mesh lid. Heat is provided by two 60 watt light bulbs which can be raised as the chicks grow away and require less heat. One light bulb only will provide sufficient heat for the chicks, but an additional bulb acts as an insurance should one bulb blow. Too many chicks have been lost overnight, when the single source of heat has let us down.

None of our brooder boxes is overlarge so we are not

Figure 6.5 Divider Pens in PHQ

Figure 6.6 Penning Room

faced with the problem of chicks huddling together in a corner, with those underneath suffocating, but should you choose to use a large box, it is advisable to pad out the corners, rounding them off. Although obviously less economical, we deliberately choose to brood small numbers of chicks together in small boxes.

Because of their small size, we rear Pekins either by themselves or with our Nankin chicks. They are never reared with the Anconas or with the Sumatra Game. Both of these breeds are more active and faster moving than the Pekins and Nankins, who tend to be bowled over by the larger chicks' quicker movements, resulting in damage and losses. Since brooding them with the Nankins we have had few fatalities from that cause.

When our chicks have outgrown the broody box, they are removed into more spacious accommodation, which incorporates a box that can be heated and a run area to give them more room. This box and run combined is in fact, an outside run or cockerel conditioning box. The lidded roof is removed and replaced by a mesh frame, through which the bulbs for heat are hung. The additional depth in this box simplifies the process of gradually reducing the heat, and chicks can remain in this unit quite happily before being moved into more permanent quarters.

As soon as chicks have been moved on into the next stage of accommodation, all previous boxes used are cleaned out, washed, disinfected and are ready for the next batch of chicks. Good management and cleanliness are imperative in these early days when the chicks are so vulnerable. It is important once again to stress the need for thorough cleaning and that painting them will make the process easier and help prevent infestation from parasites. Never store boxes away at the end of the season in a dirty condition, but have them ready and waiting for the excitement and arrival of the next year's hatch.

As our Pekins are lavender in colour and will be shown if of exhibition quality, we cannot put our growing stock outside, but should you be rearing colours which will be unaffected by the sun, they will thrive if penned in small units on short grass and can be allowed to remain outside until ready for show preparation, or, until the weather deteriorates. Pekins are very hardy, but they can be affected by too much wet weather and can be chilled if their feet are continually wet.

Our growing stock of lavender Pekins are therefore housed in the inside runs within our largest shed. Cockerels and pullets are separated at about twelve weeks, with two of the pens holding the pullets and the third the cockerels. I am very selective over which male birds I decide to grow on. Those showing obvious faults are culled as soon as the faults appear. As the numbers increase and grow away throughout the summer, space is at a premium and there is no room for obvious wasters.

LITTER

White wood shavings are excellent for both chicks and adults kept in inside pens. If your birds are light in colour, it is important to use only white shavings. The darker hard wood shavings give off a residue when wet, as I learned to my cost in the early days of keeping lavenders. The footings,

wing tips and lower feathers, once soiled and stained, remained shaded until the first moult at the end of the year.

It is good practice to clean out and provide fresh litter
BEFORE the shavings become dirty and soiled. Not only do
your birds remain clean, but also, it does deter flies which
are often the source of disease.

REARING CHICKS

Don't be fooled by their small size. Pekin chicks are
tough and as soon as they have regained their strength and
dried out after hatching, they are ready for food, water and
action. They should be left under the mother or in the rearer
for 24 hours before disturbing – other than for essential
tasks.

Born with their legs already feathered, they resemble
small, active balls of fluff. At Easter–time, I always try to
have some chicks in our shop window, under a lamp, for the
local children to see. Experience has shown that it is the
adults who are the most interested. The "oohs" and "aahs"
come from the parents, and it is the Pekin chicks, with the
feathered legs that are the most popular.

Every breeder has his own favoured methods, and perhaps, his individual secret formula for rearing chicks, and is
firmly convinced that his ways are the best.

Although the Pekin chicks are more than capable of
holding their own in the food and water stakes, as I have
already explained in the previous section, I do brood them
either separately, or with the gentler Nankins. The majority
of my chicks are hatched in the incubator, although I do keep
just three Silkie–cross Sussex hens for broodies. I haven't

Figure 6.7 Black & Lavender Chicks showing length
of feather in Black chicks

the room to keep more and I have found that too often it is the case of "sods law". I either have broodies but no eggs, or, eggs and no broodies. Only late in the season, should a Pekin go broody, do I allow the chicks to remain with the mother.

As soon as the chicks are ready for food, I initially provide them with porridge oats. They seem to manage better the softness of the oats rather than the gritty texture of chick crumbs. The food is placed in the shallow lids of jam-jars, and any chick reluctant to eat, is soon encouraged to try and peck for himself when hearing the tap of the other beaks on the metal. Within forty-eight hours, all are on chick crumbs alone, the new taste being gradually introduced by adding it to the oats. Water is essential, and is on hand as soon as they are transferred from the hatching environment and placed in the brooder.

As the chicks grow, the heat provided can be gradually reduced by raising the light bulbs, until at first it can be dispensed with altogether by day, and later, at night. You will find that the chicks will decide for themselves when they no longer require heat. At about seven or eight weeks you will discover them lying well away from the warmth.

Lavender chicks are often born with a great deal of yellow fluff amongst the pale lavender colour and I suspect that those with the greatest amount of yellow develop into adults with the desired, pale colour.

Wishing to study the growth of the Pekin chick, especially the development of the feathering, I hatched four eggs from a loaned pair - a black, mottled bred male, and a good, black female showing excellent green sheen. Both were of excellent type, the hen having been a prize winner in several shows as a pullet. The four black chicks were hatched alongside four of lavender colour.

At birth, the black chicks were noticeably larger than the lavenders and as they grew away and feathered up, it became very clear early on, that not only were the feathers on the black chicks longer in length, but that they were also broader. By four months it was very obvious that the lavender chicks had a greater abundance of fluff underneath their feathers, whilst the blacks appeared to be carrying very little fluff and seemed to be all feather.

I have retained three of the lavender chicks from that hatch, a male and two females, and one black female. The black pullet still lacks depth of fluff under the feather, yet the length and broadness of feather around the skirt, strengthens her appearance of exhibiting good tilt. The two lavender pullets have good tilt, broadness in breast and cushion, copious fluff around the thighs giving a rounded shape, yet, had they long, broad feathers in the breast area, they could have proved to be unbeatable. My goal in my future breeding programme is obvious. The broadness and length of the lavender feather must be improved, although I have no intention of introducing a black bird into the breeding. The damage this would do to the pale colour would be, in my opinion, too high a price to pay.

Pekin chicks are delightful. They appear to be fearless and are very precocious, the latter quality making them more appealing. They are unafraid of hands reaching into the brooder, indeed many will peck out at the hands that feed them. They seem to stand firm and look you straight in the eye, unlike Anconas who tend to give you a sideways look, or the Nankins with their shortsighted squint.

During growth, Pekins weather the moulting and feathering process well and few go through the bare, sparsely-feathered phase. The abundance of fluff covering them, disguises any bare patches of skin. The soft, downy feathers are in great demand by the local fishermen who come to collect them for their flies, but often the swallows and mice are quicker off the mark and their nests in our nearby farm barns are now colour co-ordinated in lavender and black.

FEEDING

CHICKS

Chicks remain on especially prepared chick crumbs which contain a medicinal additive as protection against coccidiosis, for as long as possible. At about nine weeks, rearers pellets are gradually introduced, at first for one feed, usually in the morning, and wheat mixed with the crumbs in the afternoon, until eventually, chick crumbs are no longer part of the diet. Both water and grit must be available all the time. Some breeders feed ad. lib., whereas others feed measured amounts only, twice a day. Whichever method you decide upon, it is important that Pekins are not overfed.

ADULTS

At about six months, my Pekins are introduced to a wet mash feed in the mornings. All breeders have their own ideas about methods of feeding their own stock, and often, what and how you feed is determined by the amount of time that you have available. Mash as a feed, must be freshly mixed with only sufficient water added to make a crumbly mix -- too wet, and it sticks to the beak. However, it takes time to ladle the mixture into feederss and for those who have to rush off for work, pellets are more convenient for the morning feed. We add household scraps to our mix and the birds seem to thrive on it. They certainly take a very dim view of things when we feed only pellets for quickness!

Green material such as cabbage or cauliflower leaves, lettuce, finely chopped grass and dandelion leaves are excellent for those birds that remain inside, and should be hung or placed off the floor to avoid soiling. Grit (limestone and tiny flints) is a must at all times, for the flints aid the bird's digestive processes and fresh water is also essential. Needless to say, both food and water containers must be kept clean.

Many breeders feed just wheat at night, but I mix my own grain feed, adding maize to the wheat. This is always fed as a scratch feed to all stock both inside and out. It is a good idea to add a little cod liver oil to the grain feed just once a week. Only a little is needed, sufficient to give the corn a shine. The birds enjoy it for it adds a different taste to their normal diet.

Those who breed white Pekins for exhibition, usually avoid feeding maize for it tends to yellow the feathers. Also, too much maize in the diet tends to encourage fatness, although it is very beneficial during the cold, winter months, as it is a good source of heat.

INCUBATION

A satisfactory hatch begins long before the eggs are set. Diet is important to ensure that the breeding birds are fertile; are not too fat and lazy for mating, and that the shells of the eggs are not soft through lack of grit.

When the eggs are laid, they should be collected and placed in egg trays, either sideways on, or small end downwards. The correct storage of these eggs will play an important part in ensuring that the subsequent hatching is satisfactory and they should be turned twice daily, usually, morning and night.

If you decide to use an incubator to hatch your eggs, follow the maker's instructions. Once you know your incubator, you should have few problems, but they do take a bit of getting used to.

USING A BROODY HEN

As this book is aimed at the novice breeder, I am going to assume that you will be using a broody to hatch your chicks.

You will be able to tell when a hen has gone broody. She will make a rather grumpy, clucking sound and will spend a great deal of her time in the nestbox, sometimes remaining there even when you go to feed. Allow her to remain on a few unimportant eggs to make sure that she is really broody, before risking your collected and stored eggs under her. It is advisable to move her to a quiet place, away from the other chicken. She will settle more readily and will not steal the eggs of the other birds to add to her own.

The medium for hatching successfully is one of warmth

and humidity. Make her a nest in a box that has the front cut away. This will prevent her from breaking the eggs as she clambers in and out to take food and water. Remember, she will be sitting on the eggs for twenty days , so inevitably, she will become stiff and perhaps, a little clumsy. Place an upturned turf in the bottom of the box, cover it with straw and you will have created a natural incubator for her that is both moist and warm. Dust the nest and the bird with powder to make sure that she remains comfortable throughout the twenty days she will be sitting.

Move her onto her nest and the eggs to be set, at night. This will reduce any chance of stress caused by a change in her environment, and you will find that she will settle down. You will be surprised at the heat and the dampness that are generated from the broody hen. As you lift her off for feeding, you will notice that her feathers are quite wet.

Feed her at a regular time each day and make sure that water is constantly available. After she has been sitting for about a week, "candle" the eggs by holding them in front of a bright light. Look at the egg through a hole cut out from the bottom of a shoe box. Any that are infertile, will show up clear, and those that are fertile, will already show the dark spot of the chick forming inside. Throw away the clear eggs, leaving the broody to sit only on those with chicks inside.

Remember that a broody sitting naturally in the wild, will leave the nest to feed and will have her under feathers dampened by the long grass as she moves in search of food. Therefore, as my broodies near the final two days before hatching, I spray the eggs with warm water to increase the

humidity and to soften the shells which will help the chicks
to break out more easily.

Once the chicks have started to "pip", (you will notice
a star shaped crack in the shell,) leave the hen to get on
with the hatching herself. Don't be tempted to keep going to
have a look. You will only disturb her and reduce the humidity if you keep peering under the feathers to see what is
happening.

When all the chicks have hatched, and are dried out
and fluffy, clean up the mess and debris and put down food
and water for the mother and chicks. She will encourage
them to eat when they are ready and she will look after
them, keeping them warm. Make sure that their accommodation is secure to both keep out predators and keep the
chicks confined. Use small mesh wire for runs. Pekin chicks
are very small and can easily stray through the wider holes.

As they grow and feather up, they will rely on their
mothers less and less for warmth, and indeed, she will begin
to get bored with them. Return her to her normal house with
the other Pekins and allow the chicks to grow on by themselves.

SHOWING

The local poultry show is the showcase for the birds
that you have bred and will reflect all your hard work and
skill as a breeder. Only the very best should be exhibited,
and, with Pekins, remember that *type* in your birds is of the
greatest importance and that it must take precedence over
colour.

PREPARATION

Having selected the birds that you believe are of exhibition quality, remove them from the other Pekins and pen them individually in pens, similar in size to those used in shows.

Initially, the Pekin may fly at the wire door and try to escape, but gradually she will become accustomed to her more limited space and settle down. Use your hand to steady her, placing it around her cushion to encourage her to stand still in such a way, that she exhibits her best features, ie., that she stands with her head lower than her tail. Pekin breeders never use a judging stick to move their birds, preferring to use the flat of the hand. A show judge, seen pushing his stick through the pen door at a Pekin, is guaranteed to arouse the anger of even the most gentle of Pekin breeders.

If your birds are light in colour, either white or lavender, they will already have been kept on *white* sawdust chippings. Once inside the show pen it is essential that these birds are kept clean. Hardwood chippings will stain the footings and lower feathers, and often these stains are impossible to remove.

About four days before the show, wash your bird. It is not as daunting a task as it sounds. Use good quality soap flakes in warm water, filling two bowls, one for the feet, which will be particularly dirty, and the other for the body of the bird. Scrub the feet and legs first, before transferring your Pekin to the other bowl. Hold the Pekin firmly in one hand, gripping wings and legs to prevent the bird from struggling and soaking you, and soap the bird all over, using a sponge, until you are satisfied that the feathers are clean. You will be surprised how much dirt there is in the bowl. Rinse the Pekin thoroughly, either using bowls of clean water, or a spray attachment. It is important that all the soap is removed, otherwise the feathers will feel sticky and will not shine. Wrap the bird in a towel and pat gently to absorb as much of the water as possible.

The final drying stage in the preparation of your Pekin for the show is very important, and here, methods used amongst exhibitors vary. Some advocate drying the bird as thoroughly as possible with a towel, before placing it in a box beside a warm radiator overnight to enable the feathers to dry out and to fluff up naturally. Others believe that the most successful method is to dry the bird with a hair dryer, beginning with the feet and moving to breast, back and cushion, shaping the feathers as you go. You must decide on which method you believe to be the most effective for yourself, but remember, a good Pekin can become a winning bird if your pre-show preparation is thorough.

Keep your washed Pekin as clean as possible during the final days before the show and continue to handle your bird, to encourage it to settle. The night before the show, prepare everything that you are going to need, for there will be little time the next morning.

THE SHOW

Make sure that the box or basket in which you will be transporting your bird to the show, is clean with fresh straw in the bottom. Take a damp cloth with you with which to clean the bars of the show pen. An immaculately prepared

Figure 6.8   Home from the Show
Black male owned by Clive Stephens

Figure 6.9   Be Proud of Your Success

"box" your birds. You will not be able to leave the show venue until all the exhibitors have safely boxed their birds and and, any misplaced, have been accounted for.

When you arrive home, thoroughly dust your birds with flea powder, in case they have picked up an unwelcome insect whilst at the show, give a normal feed and water, and allow them to quietly settle back into familiar surroundings. Remove the straw from the carrying box and burn it, before dusting your container with powder. Prevention now, no matter how tired you may feel, will be easier to cope with than infestation at a later stage.

Finally, be proud of the cards and the rosettes that your bird may win for you. Don't throw them in a drawer where they will lie, forgotten. Pin them up in your Pekin house to remind you of the success of your breeding programme, and of the enjoyment of travelling to shows and making fresh friends and acquaintances.

HEALTH

Pekins are no more suscectible to disease or ill health than any other breed of poultry. However, as they do tend to be kept more intensively than most other breeds, if illness does strike, it can spread rapidly.

A reference book on general poultry management will provide full details of diseases which affect poultry. However, below are some of the problems that the novice Pekin breeder may have to face.

Nothing looks more pathetic than a sick, miserable looking bird, haunched up in a corner with its feathers ruffled or staring. Good stockmanship will help to prevent

Figure 6.10 Baskets for Carrying Birds to Shows
An alternative is to use boxes which are then burnt after use.
Remember that birds require good ventilation and there should be
access to compartments for ease of moving and feeding.

illness in the first instance, and an alert fancier will recognise the warning signs early enough to be able to take immediate action.

BASIC HYGIENE PROGRAMME

Avoid unnecessary colds and chilling by ensuring that your houses are both waterproof and draughtproof and prevent stress during hot spells of weather in the summer months by ensuring that their accommodation is well ventilated and shaded from direct sun.

Young stock take a while to build up an immunity to parasites that might attack them internally.   Follow the golden rule of never running young birds on ground recently vacated by older stock.   The adult might birds show no signs of illness, yet the young stock will have little chance if exposed to the parasites left in the ground or in the litter by the adults.

Clean and disinfect all pens and runs before re-housing fresh stock.   Disinfection is most important.   It costs very little, yet it can save your birds. Prevent infestation from parasites by regularly using an insecticide and by taking great care when cleaning out.   A few parasites today can multiply into thousands very quickly.

Keep all food in covered containers to deter rats and mice who will spoil feed and who are possible transmitters of disease.

A wise fancier handles each bird regularly and inspects the vent for mite, the feathers for feather mite, and any other visible features, including the weight of the bird.

COMMON DISORDERS

COCCIDIOSIS. This is of a parasite origin and mainly affects growing birds up to 10–12 weeks; the parasite is in the intestinal tracts. Survivors are carriers. Early signs to look are: blood in the droppings; listless birds huddled in a corner and disinterest in food. A proprietary medicine which is placed in the water, can be obtained from the vet. A Coccidiostat is also found in Chick Crumbs. If not recognised early on and treatment given, death is rapid. It usually occurs when chick crumbs containing the medication are not given or are discontinued too early.

LICE AND MITE. Prevent infestation from both by dusting regularly with powder. Lice live on the birds, feeding on particles of skin and cause itching and scabbing. Mites are a more serious problem. They feed off the bird's blood at night and severe infestation can result in death through anaemia. During the day, the mites hide in darkened corners of the sheds and pens and can survive for several months in an empty house.

SCALEY LEG. Pekins are susceptible to this mite which causes thickening and encrustation of the scales on the legs. Severe infestation can make it very difficult for the birds to perch or walk. There are several remedies, but usually an application of Kerosene and linseed oil mixed in the proportion of 1:2 is effective.

IMPACTED CROP. This is often caused by the bird eating long grass. The crop feels hard to the touch and never empties, even if the bird is not fed. In my early days of keeping Pekins, I lost several birds due to their crops becoming impacted, which I now believe was caused by: (a) feeding too much grass, even though it was very finely chopped, and possibly, (b) not providing sufficient insoluble grit in the pens. Grit helps the gizzard to grind the food and if the gizzard is not functioning properly the food in the crop does not pass into the system. Now, as soon as I recognise the early signs of impaction, I immediately withdraw all grain and feed only soft food, such as bread and milk with a little added cod liver oil.

EGG BOUND. If the hen shows distress when attempting to lay and continually returns to the nest, it may be that she is bound by an abnormally large egg. Warmth and humidity will both help to relax the duct, so holding the vent of the bird over hot water to which a few drops of iodine have been added, will often prove successful. Another method is to lubricate the vent with a little warmed olive oil. Hens which are too fat, suffer from this problem and therefore the answer is to give a light diet for a while and exercise.

EGG EATING. Once a bird acquires a taste for the contents of the egg, egg eating can become a major problem. Prevent soft shelled eggs by ensuring that the birds have access to plenty of soluble grit. Often the cock birds are the main culprits. They sit and wait for the hen to vacate the nest after laying. The habit can be broken by substituting a decoy egg which, when hard boiled, had its contents removed and replaced by a mix of mustard and vinegar. The birds will probably eat the shell and mixture on the first day, but leave subsequent eggs well alone. Egg eating can be partly prevented by ensuring that egg laying areas are in the dark or nest boxes have a false bottom so the egg can roll away.

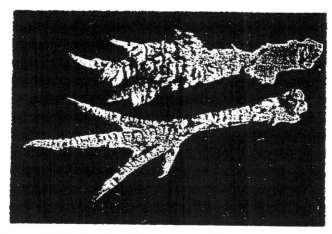

Figure 6.11 Scaley Legs on a Clean Legged Bird
The problem with feathered leg breeds is the scaliness goes
unnoticed.

Nest used for dual purpose of trapping Hen and preventing
Egg-eating.

**Figure 6.12 A Nest Box which may be used to Catch
Eggs in an Hidden False Bottom (avoids egg eating)**

BEING A STOCKMAN

So, you have read all the material that you can lay
your hands on, about setting eggs, incubation, brooding,
feeding and housing. You have talked to others about the
methods and you have discussed problems and sought advice,
but, even though you have followed instructions diligently,
you know, deep in your heart, there is something not quite
right. Your chicks, in comparison with others, don't look as
good as the breeders next door; your birds don't appear to be
as fighting fit as those in the next show pen. Why?

There is a tremendous difference between someone who
breeds and keeps Pekins and the next person who is, what I
call, a stockman. The stockman has trained himself to look
for the early signs that   all is not right: he automatically
checks his birds everytime he sees them; he constantly
handles them; he is aware if their droppings are not normal
or if the bird has gone off its feed; he is prepared to cull his
birds if they fail to match up to his high standards, or if they
show obvious defects; and his care for his stock is not blinded
by sentimentality.

Only by being constantly concerned about their welfare, vigilant if things are wrong and aware that stress of
any kind will cause your birds to be under-par, will you be
able to raise sound, healthy stock, and, in turn, gain the
reputation amongst fanciers, of being a good breeder of Pekins, and, an excellent stockman.

CHAPTER SEVEN

PEKIN CHARACTERISTICS
AND STORIES.

Pekins give endless hours of enjoyment to the people who keep them, whether these owners are interested in improving the breed and exhibiting their stock, or choosing to keep this delightful bred because they find them so interesting.

In turn, Pekins do seem to enjoy contact with their owners and respond in such a way, that all the work involved in their care is more than rewarded by the pleasure they give. Just as magpies have been labelled "the villains of the birdworld," Pekins have the accolade of being the true characters of the poultry world. Stories concerning their idiosyncrasies which endear them to us are endless and are told, not only by fanciers who could be labelled as being sentimentalists, but also by experienced breeders of long standing.

Talking to Pekins is guaranteed to elicit a response, the female greeting being a "whup, whup" in the case of my own birds, which I now believe to be a learned response.

My first pair of lavender Pekins, *Darby* and *Joan*, were originally housed in a shed at the far end of the garden. On seeing me approach, Joan invariably greeted me with her "whup, whup" sound. When her chicks were hatched they were housed in another shed, nearer to the house, well out of earshot of the noises emitted by the mother.

The chicks grew away, but none ever greeted me in the same way as their mother. Two females from that hatch remained for breeding and the three birds were penned together. In time, I realised that the newcomers had begun to copy Joan's greeting every time I approached their house.

My male Pekins are particularly vociferous when they hear footsteps on the gravel which surrounds their house, bantam headquarters, or B.H.Q., as it has become known. This is noticeable first thing in the morning before unlocking. Before I reach the gravel, all is quiet, but on hearing the first crunch underfoot, pandemonium breaks out. Early visitors would be amazed to see me creeping along the flags on the path and gingerly stepping on the gravel, trying to avoid the tell-tale sound in my attempts to surprise them, -- it never works.

The males are exuberant in their greeting, puffing themselves up to look twice their normal size, pounding the ground with their feet whilst turning in slow circles, like primitive warriors performing a ritual war dance. The females, however, more restrained and ladylike in their actions, wait until I come into sight, before greeting me with their characteristic, "whup, whup".

The males in particular, wage a constant war against magpies and crows. They are able to spot them when they are some distance away, perched on the telephone wires or a windblown bush, and can be guaranteed to vent their feelings against them with a tirade of shrill screams and abuse. If our elderly siamese cat ventures inside B.H.Q., she is given a similar reception to that given to the magpies and crows,

Figure 7.1   Keeping Watch

Figure 7.2   Bantam of the Opera

but outside, Pekins and neighbourhood cats have at last reached a truce.

I have also found Pekins to be excellent watchdogs. They seem to have the ability to recognise the crunch of unfamiliar tyres on the gravel and give out the warning sounds to alert us that visitors have arrived.

As well as responding vocally when spoken to, Pekins do seem to enjoy company. They always appear especially content when someone is working in their shed, maybe cleaning out, constructing new pens or undertaking repairs. Many times I've been concentrating on the task at hand, and suddenly become aware that all is silent, and that I am being solemnly watched by several pairs of curious eyes.

Inquisitive by nature, they will strain to look at you from their pens until, realising that you in turn are watching them, they delight in a noisy display of stamping and in the uttering of hair-raising shrieks.

In my early days of keeping lavenders, I had a spare cockerel, but too few females. Unwilling to pen him alone, I ran him with three Silkie cross Sussex hens that I kept for broodies. His antics whilst living with his white companions gave us many laughs. When the pophole was raised first thing in the morning, he was always to the fore in the rush out for the grass. He then followed the normal stamping war dance display prior to mating, attempting to mount each female in turn. It was wasted effort on his part. He found them insurmountable and he inevitably rolled off their broad backs in an undignified manner, but he never gave up.

Almost without exception, they are extremely gentle. I know of only one instance of a male Pekin who was, to quote the owner, "Determined to take my hands off!" Sometimes, the chicks become over-enthusiastic when being fed, pecking at anything offered, fingers and hands included, but they soon outgrow this trait and generally enjoy being handled.

The male birds of many breeds become fiercely protective of their hens if you choose to invade their territory. I am most certainly not prepared to put my head into my pen of bantam Anconas at breeding time, for I know only too well, that the cock bird will fly at me in defence of his females and his space. There will always be a few rogues in every breed, but the gentleness of Pekins is well-known, making them particularly suitable to be kept by children as their first introduction into poultry keeping. They are usually treated as well loved pets and are as much at home on their young owners' laps in front of the T.V., as they are in their pens outside.

They are not, however, so gentle with one another. Putting females together can be a problem, for they often show aggression towards each other and can be spiteful. Yet, given space, a nest box in which the bird at the end of the pecking order can take refuge, - and time, they will live in companionable harmony.

When becoming broody and allowed to sit on her eggs, the temperament of the normally docile hen changes. Her puffed up feathers and fanned tail make her look twice her normal size and she immediately becomes an aggressive ball of fury in defence of her eggs and later, her young. Her bad tempered clucking is more than adequate warning to stand clear.

The males appear to take an interest in the "domestic"

side of Pekin life. They seem to take a pride in the hens laying and will often be found in the nest box themselves, making similar sounds to those made by the female when she is laying. Many times I have seen the cock bird jumping in and out of the nest box as if encouraging the hen to get on with the job.

There are stories, too, of the male being involved in brooding. One season, reluctant to allow a broody hen to go unused, but short of space to set her on eggs elsewhere, I allowed a female Pekin to sit on her eggs in a corner of the house. The cock bird stood guard over her, shared her nest at night and was once found sitting on the eggs himself whilst she ate and drank. I was sure that the eggs would be doomed, but as they were not vital in my breeding programme, I allowed them to get on with things unhindered and between them, they somehow hatched and brought up their young.

This is not a method of incubation to be recommended or followed, but it does clearly illustrate just one of the extraordinary characteristics found in the make-up of the Pekin that makes them such a very special breed.

Dick Ricketts, former secretary to the Pekin Club, today a well known judge, wrote to me with a similar story:

> "The only case I have ever seen of a cock brooding chicks, was a black Pekin. To me it looked strange to see a rather macho male proudly sitting in a nest box, with a large brood of chicks peeping out from under him. It truly was a picture of a proud dad showing off his family."

Figure 7.3 Author's Cuckoo Cockerel

Figure 7.4 Young Lavender Pullet bred by the Author

but the lady who owned the black Pekin cock said that it was the second year that he had taken on the task.

An excellent example of the Pekin's enjoyment of being in the company of their owners, is the story sent to me by Mr and Mrs Hancox, from Sussex. Now retired, they have time to spend with their buff Pekins, who like nothing better than to encourage their owners to spend time sitting in the garden. No sooner do Mr and Mrs Hancox settle themselves in the sun, than the Pekins fly up onto their laps, enjoy a gentle stroke and survey their surroundings from loftier heights. Their buffs give them hours of pleasure.

We know that the broody hen will defend eggs and chicks to the last. Jessica and Lee Manion, who were given their buff Pekins for pets, tell the lovely story of their female, named "Bantam of the Opera," who, on becoming broody, was given a set of duck eggs to hatch. Unfortunately a female Buff Orpington became broody at the same time.

> **"The battle was on,"** they wrote. **"Who would win to hatch the eggs, the giant Orpington or Bantam of the opera?"**
>
> **Pekins may be small, but there was no contest.**
> **Bantam of the Opera raised four lovely ducklings.**

There are similar stories of the Pekin male, finding himself in a threatening situation, being more than prepared to defend his own corner and, in the majority of circumstances, coming out on top. Dick Ricketts contributes another story, this time illustrating the male Pekin's ability to defend his own position.

In the 1950's, Dick gave his brother a surplus buff cockerel. As there was a shortage of room, the cockerel was housed with half a dozen large cockerels which were being fattened for Christmas. The next morning, when his brother went to feed them, he discovered the six, large cockerels huddled together in a corner, with "Buffy" Pekin strutting up and down in front of them, daring them to move. Although he was half their size, he was "cock of the walk." Buffy was soon found a home of his own, to protect the family's Christmas dinner as much as anything.

Only recently, I've had reason to be more than grateful to my Pekins. Always heralders of alarm within the shed, they alerted my husband to a crisis. Owing to a sharp spell of cold weather, I brought a promising pair of late hatched bantam Sumatra Game male chicks into the Pekin shed. There were penned in one of the three large runs, with Pekins on either side of them.

The usual morning feed for my adult stock consists of a mash, supplemented by household scraps, but on this particular morning I had an early business appointment, so they were fed pellets. My husband was already at work in the workshop, and he suddenly became aware of an unusually frantic, cacophony of sound coming from B.H.Q. He stepped inside the door, but the clamour continued. This was unusual, for their noise generally ceases on our approach, so he investigated further.

One of the Sumatra males was giving a final lurch before falling into the litter, legs in the air. My husband's desperate shout brought me running. The chick had a mass of pellet mixture in his throat and was unable to breathe. I squeezed and hooked out of the wet mass, whilst David rubbed the bird's chest and we were relieved when at last, he began to take in air in small gasps.

He spent the whole morning looking very sorry for himself penned in a box in David's warm workshop and made a full recovery, but had it not been for the Pekins, we would have lost him.

Boogie, my youngest male, is not fond of pellets in the morning feed and makes his objection abundantly clear. On discovering that he has not been given his warm, morning mash, he utters a furious shriek, picks up the plastic feeding bowl with his beak and hurls it to the back of the pen. He then stands in the corner with his back towards me, his stance telling me exactly what he thinks of the menu.

Everyone who keeps Pekins must have numerous stories about their own birds' idiosyncrasies and odd little ways. It is these endearing examples of their characters that give us so much pleasure and make them such a popular breed.

INDEX

■ ■

INDEX